Panda Books
The Black Button

Liang Xiaosheng was born in September 22, 1949 in Harbin into a working-class family. After leaving junior high school he became first a farm-worker and then a teacher in a primary school. He graduated from the Chinese Department of Fudan University in 1977 and subsequently worked as an editor and playwright at the Beijing Film Studio. He is now working at the China Children's Film Studio. A number of his works published after 1978 have been adapted for film and TV. Several, including "A Land of Wonder and Mystery" and "Father" have won literary awards.

The Black Button

Liang Xiaosheng

Panda Books

Panda Books
First Edition 1992
. Copyright 1992 by CHINESE LITERATURE PRESS
ISBN 7−5071−0116−9
ISBN 0−8351−3126−2

Published by CHINESE LITERATURE PRESS
Beijing 100037, China
Distributed by China International Book Trading Corporation
35 Chegongzhuang Xilu, Beijing 100044, China
P.O. Box 399, Beijing, China
Printed in the People's Republic of China

CONTENTS

Preface

FOUR stories and one novelette are included chronologically in this publication: "The Jet Ruler" is one of my early endeavours; "A Land of Wonder and Mystery", "Father" and "The Black Button" were written in a stage of rapid development, and "Ice Dam" was completed in 1988.

Literature is part of my life. The realities of life in China form the basis of my writing. For a mature novelist, reality is more than what is happening in the present or what is going to happen in the future. Reality also represents, I believe, the bedrock as well as the evolution of a culture or period of history, and is a prelude to the future. I sincerely hope that works by Chinese writers may serve as a window through which other cultures may observe the developments of events in our country.

Good works by writers from abroad exert a positive influence on Chinese writers, myself included. As the old adage goes, "Advice from others may help one to overcome one's own weaknesses."

A good work of literature cannot be confined within national boundaries. Literature is a universal means of communication.

I respect translators, Chinese or foreign, whether they translate a foreign language into Chinese or vice versa, for they have built bridges for mankind.

Pacifism, humanism, people and reality — these have been my guidelines in my life as a writer. I will not bend in the face of harsh criticism from those who follow certain modern trends.

May literature forever be a benign source of influence on the hearts and minds of the Chinese people. I firmly believe this is a difficult, though by no means impossible, task.

The Jet Ruler

SHE turned towards the coal mine, where the majestic slag was like a pyramid wreathed in dense mist. The rising sun, blazing red and wheel-shaped, was suspended just above the slag, as if it had been hauled up to the sky by a thick cable.

Suddenly she thought of him. Today was an even-numbered day, and he should be down in the pit with the other miners. If it hadn't been for him, she would not have come here. Tomorrow she was going to leave, not knowing whether she would ever return.

One day four months ago, while her family were having supper, he had knocked at their door.

She had opened it and sized him up — a complete stranger, aged around thirty, strapping and broad-faced, with rough yet well-defined features. What a handsome man! She thought, impressed. Just the image of the King of Spades. Better if he had a beard. She had her particular aesthetic standards, and thought of the King as the ultimate in masculine beauty. What a pity he didn't have a beard!

She stood in the doorway, eyeing him with unconcealed appreciation, then asked politely, "What do you want?"

His reply was three words — her father's name.

"Come in, please," she said, making way for him.

He stepped inside and strode three paces to cross the hallway into the room. The whole family marvelled and wondered, their eyes focused on this unexpected visitor.

He explained vaguely, "I'd like to have a word with Bureau Chief Yan, about some business, if ..."

Her father put down his chopsticks immediately and led him into the living room.

About a dozen minutes later, her father walked him to the door, where they heard Father ask, "Are you a leader of the mine?"

"Is that important?" the visitor replied. "Take me as a spokesman for the miners."

When the man had left, Father called her into the living room, and asked her what she meant to do after graduation. She replied correctly that she was ready to serve wherever she was needed as a teacher. "That's the stuff." Father nodded appreciatively. "That's the way to think." Then, in the solemn tone of a superior addressing his subordinate at work, he said, "Well, it's like this. Because I'm the chief of the education bureau and you're my daughter, a graduate of the teachers' training college, and because the mine is in urgent need of school-teachers, you ought to volunteer to work there. I'm going to your college to give a pep talk, and I want you to set an example. Without volunteers, what I say will just be a lot of hot air. Do you understand?"

Yes, she understood, too well to utter a single word. What wonderful logic! And that damn "King" had come here to trap her!

She cried, whimpered, pleaded and lost her temper. She implored her mother to intercede and her sister to protest on her behalf, but it was all in vain. Her father was firm and always gave the same answer, "You are not plunging into hell teaching at the mine." What a cold heart!

At last, against her will, she "volunteered".

She received a warm welcome the day she arrived at the mine. Descending from the train, her eyes spotted the "King" among the welcomers. Resenting him, she pretended not to see him.

He strode up to her, and held out a large hand to grasp her tiny one, saying, "I didn't expect to see you!" Then he proceeded with a series of introductions: the chairman of the trade union, the head of the women's association, the secretary of the Youth League and the primary school principal — all the prominent figures in the district. Even if she had been the minister of the Coal Industry himself, there could not have been a better turn-out of people to do the honours. That she was so important in their eyes was quite beyond her imagination.

The chairman of the trade union, pointing at the "King", said to her, "This is head of the mine. You know each other?"

So he was her immediate superior!

"I wouldn't say I know him," she replied coldly, glaring at him. "We met only once."

At her first dinner in the mine, the "King" sat beside her. He told her gravely, "You're the first graduate from the teachers' training college to come to this district. Our primary school was set up not long ago and it's in great need of trained teachers. But nobody wants to teach here even if we invite them. You're the first to come, so I'd like to express our respect and gratitude to you on behalf of the miners. I hope you can understand this.''

He uttered the word ''understand'' in a solemn tone, then paused, as if considering whether she could bear the weight of it.

Instead of being angry, she smiled. His formal, logical way of speaking reminding her of her father. Perhaps his school teacher had been too strict with his grammar.

He smiled too, and that lightened the atmosphere.

''If you've no objection, tomorrow I'd like to accompany you down the pit,'' he said. ''You haven't been in a cage, have you?''

''I was in something like it in a park when I was small.''

''Going down the pit in a cage gives you a sense of adventure. Of course, that's only the first time. Anyway, it may revive your childhood memories.''

When she was first given a miner's overalls, her spirits sank at the sight of the coarse dirty canvas with its strong smell of sweat. She decided not to remove her own clothes but to wear the overall on top of them. Though it was summer, she could stand the heat, whereas the feeling of the rough canvas rubbing against her delicate skin was something unthinkable.

He noticed her decision, but did not sneer at her. Instead he gave an understanding smile.

The safety helmets were differentiated by four colours: red, green yellow and black. The regulations written on a board, which she read with interest, were as follows: the black helmets are for the miners, the yellow for cadres, the red for safety inspectors and the green for people on temporary errands.

The storeman handed them two helmets. He helped her on with one of them, as well as a miner's lamp and a belt to which was fastened a battery.

The miners waiting for the cage hailed him from a distance. They teased him, but he took no offence, as if quite used to it. He grasped one joker's arm and wrenched it behind him until he bent down and protested, "What a bully you are, boss!" Then he let it go with a triumphant smile.

The cage rattled up and stopped at the pit-head. The moment she took a seat in it, three young men rushed over jostling to sit next to her. She ended up squeezed like a gecko against the cage's cold iron frame.

When he noticed this, he came up without a word and dragged the men away by the collar one by one. Then he seated himself beside her while the three young men resignedly sat elsewhere.

The cage stopped once halfway down. She saw the three young men get out, heading for a newly-opened face.

He showed her round the pit, with which he was so familiar, like a surgeon showing interns the blood vessels in a human body. He related the mine's history, the structure of the seam. Proudly he told her that their output was the highest in the district. Then he explained to her how the machinery functioned, about working underground and safety measures. He was such a patient guide that she was surprised. If she hadn't come, she would never have got so much specialized knowledge.

She could not help admiring him.

"Do you often go down the pit with the miners?"

"Yes, almost every day," he said. "I'm from a miner's family. Both my grandfather and father were miners, and I myself was head of a team at the age of eighteen."

"Do you think the miners respect you now that you're the head of the mine?"

No sooner were the words out of her mouth than she could have bitten her tongue off, recalling the way the miners teased him on the surface. She could not see his face, nor imagine his expression, but she discerned two sparkling eyes unmistakably resting on her. How bright they were! This discovery made her heart miss a beat. Now in this dark place there were only the two of them, a frail girl and a sturdy man. She thought of those rough-mannered youths and was so disturbed that in a moment of nervousness she knocked her lamp against the face, shattering the glass. There was total blackness everywhere.

"What's wrong with you?" His voice came out of the darkness.

"Don't, don't come over!" she cried panic-stricken.

He turned on his own lamp and handed it to her silently. Then he said calmly, "Let's go up now. You look a bit tired." After that he turned to go without looking at her.

She was exhausted. Her clothes, soaked with perspiration and sticking to her skin, made her feel uncomfortable. He strode ahead with steps twice as long as hers and she had to hurry to keep up with him. What she feared now was being left behind in the dark pit.

He paused to wait for her and gave her enough time

to catch her breath. When they resumed walking, she asked remorsefully and timidly, "You're not angry with me, are you?"

Without looking back, he replied, "For what?"

"For the question I asked you just now. Perhaps, perhaps...." But in her heart she knew that if he was really annoyed with her, it was not because of her question. Moreover, he had good reason to be angry with her, even to curse her.

For some time he went on walking in silence, then said, "As far as I understand, your question concerns my prestige. I admire Manager Qiao* and would love to be a leader like him, but I know I can't, at least, as far as my relationship with the miners is concerned. When I put on a safety helmet, I like the men to feel I'm just one of them. I drink and play finger-guessing games with them. We call each other brother, and even swear together.... Half my wages goes on wine and cigarettes. Miners are not like workers in other enterprises. No, they're different. I must understand this. I'm only glad they think I'm not such a bad manager. Apart from that, I've no other desires. As for my own prestige, maybe the primary school-teacher can explain it better than me. I don't care — "

He said these words slowly, sustaining the same calm tone, in which she could sense a melancholy kind of self-confidence.

When they reached a bend in the tunnel, he jumped

---

*Manager Qiao is a fictional character in "Manager Qiao Assumes Office", a popular story by Jiang Zilong (see *Chinese Literature*, No. 2, 1980).

forward abruptly and pushed three miners working there into an emergency hollow. Blocking the opening with his large body, he said to her casually, "Go ahead. Nothing to be seen here." But she had seen, by the miners' lamps, three naked bodies covered in perspiration and coal dust. Lowering her head, she hastily brushed past him. She remembered clearly this was where the three young men had got out of the cage.

Stepping in front of her, he asked coldly, "What's the matter?"

She only shook her head.

He lowered his head thinking for a moment, then said, "I've no right to punish them for this. Our production is modernized, but we still can't do away with spades and picks entirely. Not long ago, there was a gas explosion right here with two miners buried alive in the pit...." He paused, his hand gently touching the solid coal, and went on in an extremely low voice, "They were both in their twenties, and they were knocked down by a blast wave with a force of nine kilogrammes per square centimetre! It sliced through the coal like a knife. While there was still great danger those three young miners volunteered to try and rescue their fellow-workers and prevent a further disaster. They worked non-stop for three days. Their skins were so raw and bruised, swollen and inflamed, that even now they can't wear clothes at work...."

"Oh, stop it!" she burst out. "But you're the head, how can you bear to see the men working in such dirty clothes?"

His head bent, and in an even heavier voice, he replied, "We're a mine, not a laboratory. Three shifts a day, hundreds of miners a shift, comes to thousands of clothes. I'd like to issue the men clean clothes every day, but I'm not superhuman."

She was grieved to see this big man's face take on a look of helplessness.

With a wry smile, he went on, "There wasn't enough time for the miners to have their lunch up on the surface, so I decided on my own to provide them with a free lunch worth thirty fen underground, but I twice had to make self-criticisms over it. It was not until a comrade from the Central Committee inspected us and made a decision that my case was dismissed.'

"I beg your pardon, I didn't know..." she said mildly, touching his big hand with her small one, as a gesture of conciliation to lessen a little the gap between them.

Up on the surface, the sunlight was so dazzling that she could hardly open her eyes. She staggered a few steps, then vomited.

That evening, she came to his office and offered to start work the next day. He showed neither surprise nor admiration at her initiative. She wanted to sit longer in his office and just chat with him, but sensing his bad mood, she felt obliged to leave. Then she noticed he had been holding a black ruler. Aware of her curiosity, he explained, "Originally it was a bar of jet which I found down in the pit. Whenever I was thinking, I would stand by the window and rub it against the cement windowsill. After a long time, it turned into this ruler. When I've done something useful for the men, I carve a notch on it. Now it not only has scales in centimetres but also in millimetres...."

On her way back to the mine, she thought: I wonder whether he has carved a notch for my coming here.

No, it's not possible. Anyway, what am I compared with those miners working underground? Do I occupy a place in their minds?

The school had a few simple teaching materials, something she had expected. But what offended her self-respect as a teacher was her pupils. When she was in the teachers' training college, she had been told in her first class that children were the flowers of the country. But here, packed into the classroom were children with dirty little faces and hands. Most of them wore clothes either too large or too tight, or missing some buttons. Some had their toes peeping out of the front of their shoes. The hair of some of the boys was so long that they could wear plaits.... If there was anything bright about them, it was their eyes, which shone with liveliness and intelligence.

The moment she stepped into the classroom, they chorused, "Good morning, teacher!"

She couldn't help frowning at their strong local accent.

"Good morning, children," she replied. Then she tried to correct their pronunciation. "Now look at my mouth — *tea* — *cher* —"

Then she called on a boy to say it after her.

A few giggles came from the class.

She was angry, "Stop laughing!"

The children were awed into silence, staring at her. They wondered why she was so hard on them for their pronunciation the very first day.

"Who taught you to read this way?"

"Miss Li," replied a pupil timidly. "She's gone to have a baby."

She was so disgusted at the prospect of being a

teacher in a place like this that she declared, "Today I can't give you any lessons, because you've made me too sad. Tomorrow I want you to come to school neat and clean."

Bending their heads, the children passed before her, filing out of the classroom.

She was the last to leave. At the door, she found the head of the mine and the school principal.

"I hope you don't mind," she said first to the principal. "As a teacher, I believe it is my duty to help my pupils cultivate the good habit of cleanliness."

The principal was in his fifties and had on dirty clothes himself. He scratched his jaw and said, "Of course, of course. But—" He cast a glance at the head of the mine.

Then she turned to the latter, "I hope you can understand this."

He had just lit a cigarette. Gazing at it, he said, "Perhaps you're right."

Why perhaps? she thought. Anyway, I don't care whether it's right or wrong, I'll insist. She wouldn't give way on the first day.

"Goodbye," she said and went off without a backward glance.

At nine that evening, she went out for a walk before getting ready for bed, and happened to see the head of of the mine lead a dozen children out of the workers' bathhouse towards the office building.

Immediately it dawned upon her. She followed them and crept upstairs until she came to a clossed door. Peeping through a glass pane in the door she saw some brand-new children's clothes stacked on the desk.

He was dividing the clothes. After they were all

handed out, he said, "Now you put them on and let me have a look." Then he sat back in a chair, smoking and watching the children change their clothes.

When they had finished, he ordered, "Come here."

They gathered round him obediently.

"Hold out your hands."

They did so. Stubbing out his cigarette, he found a tiny pair of scissors and began cutting their nails.

She thought of walking in, but hesitated, lacking courage.

When he cut the nails of a girl whose head had been shaved, he asked, "Why did you cut off all your hair?"

"I had lice," the girl murmured. "Uncle, I'm afraid of the new teacher. I'm sure she won't like my bald head."

"You needn't be afraid. She's a good teacher. She'll like you." On second thoughts, he added, "She'll write her a letter. Can you take it to her tomorrow?"

"Yes, I can."

A boy blurted out, "Uncle, do you like the teacher?"

This child's question shocked him for a moment, then he shook his head, smiling.

She felt her self-respect had never been so seriously injured. Retreating step by step to the landing, she raced downstairs and ran all the way to the dormitory.

The next day, the girl with the shaved head brought her a letter. It read: "This girl's father died in the course of his work. If she makes some mistakes which annoy you, I beg you to control yourself. Everybody in the mine, adult or child, sympathizes with her and would take the blame to protect her, would take your scolding or even curses. As for her hair, it'll soon grow back again and she'll have beautiful long black hair.''

Although the letter fulfilled its purpose and she became very concerned about the girl, never losing her temper with her, she was ill at ease, because she could read his coldness between the polite lines.

From that day on, she never took the initiative in speaking or greeting him. Then something happened.

The school didn't have special rooms for the teachers, so she lived in the bachelors' dormitory. As a favour, she was given a room to herself at the farthest end of the corridor on the third floor. Whenever the men met her in the corridor or in the bathroom, they acted courteously. They called her "teacher", and when she went out to do morning exercises on the balcony, they too swung their arms or stretched their legs. One evening, she shut herself up listening to music on her tape recorder, but after a while she couldn't refrain from dancing. Then she seemed to hear some movement outside her door. Stopping, she stared at the door. The next moment, the corridor resounded with the retreating footsteps of several people. Furious, she opened the door to find no one there. She returned to sit on the bed and decided to take her revenge on those forward young men.

The next time she was dancing, the same thing happened. She pretended not to notice anything and went on dancing but edged towards the door. Suddenly she squatted down and blew into the keyhole. At once there was a commotion outside, and she had to bite her lip to hold back her laughter. She knew the chalk powder she had put into the keyhole would have given them something to think about.

She felt she ought to report this action to the head of the mine. At noon one day, he came to the dormitory, assembled all the bachelors and made them line up in two rows in the corridor. Like a commander reviewing his troops, he clasped his hands behind his back and walked to and fro in front of them. Then he stopped to point at the bloodshot eyes of one young man, "It was you, wasn't it?"

The "criminal" bent his head in humiliation, his expression one of pitiful resignation.

"Your eyes, have you been to the clinic about them?"

"There was no need."

"Can you go to work in the pit?"

"Yes."

"Nonsense! You can't work underground with red eyes, you good-for-nothing!"

Hearing his harsh words, she felt sorry. She came out, walked up to him and said, "I'm to blame too...."

He shot a glance at her, saying, "What measures I take are none of your business." Then he called a man over to paint a white line on the floor in front of her door.

Pointing to it he declared, "Beyond this line is out of bounds, you understand?"

"Yes," the young men replied.

"You're dismissed."

She darted into her room, closed the door, threw herself on the bed, and had a good cry.

After that, whenever they came across her, they acted as if they had met a tiger and quickly took to their heels. The line separating them from her had, in fact, placed her in solitary confinement. Whenever she went to the dormitory after work she seldom took a step outside her room.

But the situation lasted only a week when the rule was broken by the maker himself. One day he crossed the line to knock at her door. She opened it and, hesitating, thought of shutting it in his face. After a moment when they'd stared into each other's eyes however, she let him in, though the look on her face was as frosty as ever.

He stated bluntly that he wanted her to teach him to dance. She refused, thinking it absurd that he should suggest it after having taken measures to protect her. But he didn't mind. With a smile, he explained that the mine was to sponsor a party with the women workers of the cotton mill, and he had made all the arrangements. He hoped that at the party some miners would find girlfriends.

The explanation was above-board. At last, though still reluctant, she agreed.

"Are you going to find a wife for yourself at the party too?" she asked.

"No, but I'd like to learn to dance in case I have to start the ball rolling."

Although big, he was not clumsy. On the contrary he was quick to learn. After some practice, he could dance quite gracefully.

Finally, he assigned her a task: she was to coach the dancers and teach them some social graces.

The day of the party arrived. The bachelors, all decently turned out and in high spirits, got on to several trucks heading for the cotton mill.

Several such parties were organized, but the desired result was not achieved, nor did there seem any prospect of it. The girls' attitude was clear: You can have as many parties as you like, and we're quite ready to dance or even be friends with you. But as for being the wife of a miner — no, that's out of the question.

She felt it necessary to comfort him.

As was his habit, he beat the jet ruler softly on his palm for a long time, then said, "I've never been beaten so badly."

Seeing such a self-confident man reduced to depression touched her deeply.

From then on, she believed that she had begun to understand him.

Now it was vacation time and she was going home. But she felt upset. She couldn't decide whether or not she would return the next term, for she had not been prepared to stay long in the mine when she first agreed to work there. Certainly she could work there for a time as a duty, but it was unthinkable that she would devote her whole life to teaching there. At any rate, she had already been at the place several months, and now it was someone else's turn to experience life there.

However, human feelings are complex. When the time finally arrived for Robinson Crusoe to bid farewell to the desert island on which he had been stranded, he might have felt some regret at leaving. She had to admit to herself that there was something here she hated to part with. But she was not Robinson Crusoe and the mine was not a desolate island in the ocean, nor were the miners savages.

The miners were more like Prometheus. The civilization that people enjoy today was, to some extent, thanks to their grimy backs, whereas society had given them so little in return. She knew that even if she left the mine for good, she would never swear, as she had done formerly, if the heating was not on as early as it should be. Never again! On the contrary, she would rather cut down on her consumption of boiled water in order to save a lump of coal.

Leaving the dormitory with her holdall, she avoided the reception room at the courtyard gate. Instead, she went out through a hole in the fence. She took all her clothes, but left her new quilt and a note, on which she wrote that she might not return, and that she hoped the head of the mine would give it to the girl with the shaved head. To avoid meeting people, she chose the longer way to the railway station.

As she walked, she thought of the jet ruler. "If you were to measure people's hearts with it, I wonder how many would have a clean conscience." Her heart was heavy.

Nearing the station, she happened to look up and caught a glimpse of a man hurrying towards it. In one arm he carried a child, in the other a large parcel. It was the leader of the mine and the girl. Suddenly she felt so confused that she wished she could flee or hide herself somewhere.

But it was too late. He was approaching and in a moment stood right in front of her.

"The janitor told me that you'd gone," he said. "I took your quilt to the girl's home as you wished, but her mother refused to accept it, though she was very grateful to you. The mine administration had just given them three quilts, so I've brought it back to you. She wants to say goodbye to you too."

He spoke in the same calm tone, avoiding any expression of regret at her leaving, nor trying to persuade her to stay. If he had stated this, or even dropped a hint, she might have told him without hesitation, "I'll be back!"

The little girl had been looking at her in a knowing way. She asked timidly, "Teacher, do you want to leave because you don't like to see a girl without hair? If so, I'll wait till my hair grows long enough to wear plaits before I go to school. Is that all right?" Her eyes rested upon her eagerly waiting for her reply.

He put down the child and said to her gently, "Don't be silly. Our teacher is leaving. Now bow to her."

The girl bowed politely. When she raised her head again, her eyes were full of tears.

The train's whistle shrieked in the distance.

Taking a step towards her, he took out the jet ruler and said, "Please accept it as a souvenir. There's a notch on it I carved for you."

For a moment she hesitated to take it, staring at him in disbelief.

"I meant what I said."

She took the ruler in silence, feeling it heavier than ever. She had not expected that her value was also marked on the jet ruler. For a moment she felt she was so petty that she really didn't deserve it.

"If you decide not to return, I'll see that your file is transferred. Don't worry."

The train drew into the station. She got on with her

bag, and he handed her the quilt. Standing at the door, she felt the urge to speak some last words to him, but not knowing what to say, she merely staring at them woodenly.

The train moved off, leaving them behind side by side on the receding platform. She saw the girl's arm raised.

Tears suddenly welled up in her eyes and she cried out, "I'll be back!"

But the train was already too far off, and they didn't hear her.

Translated by Yang Nan

A Land of Wonder and Mystery

IT was a deathly silent and boundless swamp, covered the whole year round with dried branches, rotten leaves, and poisonous algae. The surface, dark brown and stagnant, had a deceptively peaceful appearance. Below it was an oozing abyss which contained the decomposing skeletons of bears, hunters' guns and tractors belonging to reclamation teams. It sent out a morbid odour for a hundred *li* and was known as Spirits' Swamp.

When I first arrived in that Great Northern Wilderness, I heard many legends about this Spirits' Swamp: deep in the starless, moonless night one could see across the slumbering wasteland the eerie greenish glow of the will-o'-the-wisps; one could hear bears roar as they were swallowed by the swamp, gunshots fired by hunters for help and the desperate cries of those caught in the mire ... sometimes one could hear a strange bird song which sounded just like a sad woman's wailing "What a pity, what a pity ..." but no one had ever seen what kind of bird it was. The local Oroqen people called it the bird which "summons back the spirits". They thought that it was really an incarnation of the God of the Earth and that deep in the night it came to comfort and call back the spirits of people and animals who had died in Spirits' Swamp. And the will-o'-the-wisps were its lanterns.

Spirits' Swamp, like the ferocious nine-headed drag-on of Greek myth, forcibly occupied the land behind it, a fertile land of more than ten thousand hectares, and no one dared cross the swamp to reclaim it. The Oroqen people used to call this land the "Devil's Reach". During winters they occasionally crossed it, but they never killed any animals for fear of inescapable punishment by the "Devil".

It was my third winter in the Great Northern Wilder-ness. A detachment of a dozen or so educated youths had been sent by our reclamation company to Devil's Reach.

As a result of being wrongly sited at the outset, our company was located in a natural depression with fair-ly limited arable land. If harvest happened to coincide with a rainy season, the combine harvesters got bogged down in the wheat fields like paralysed toads. So we had always had bad harvests and that particu-lar year could not even produce enough for the follow-ing years' seeds. We couldn't afford to live off the land, much less send grain to the state. That was why the reclamation regiment decided to disband our compa-ny and re-allocate the more than two hundred young people to other companies.

What more profound humiliation could there be than this decision? Many of us burst into tears as we lis-tened to the old company leader's announcement. Li Xiaoyan, the company's deputy instructor, was the first to stand up and indignantly refute the decision.

"The company should not be broken up! We can re-claim Devil's Reach. We ought to have thought of it earlier. We must rebuild our company there. Let Devil's Reach be covered with our reclaimers' footprints for the first time. We'll guarantee the regiment that we'll get a crop the same year we reclaim the land. The following year we'll have our new company base. Take our word for it!"

Though usually we listened indifferently to her ambitious words, this time her rousing speech actually did encourage us and many of us felt the same way.

Finally the regiment cancelled their decision and accepted our guarantee.

Several days later, we set off with two first-rate 54 h.p. tractors decorated with red ribbons and flowers, a newly made wooden sled trailing behind each for the vast snow-covered wilderness. The whole company had lined up to see us off. Hope, confidence, trust and a silent concern were in their eyes, and each of us felt a strong sense of responsibility. Everyone cried.

The first sled held our food and luggage and we squeezed ourselves into the tent set up on the second.

We sat silently shoulder to shoulder. Beside me my younger sister cuddled a wicker cage which contained a small squirrel. She looked pale, her expression dull, her eyes sad and, like a deaf-mute, said nothing the whole journey. I had no other brothers or sisters. Although I had loved her very much since childhood, I felt a mixture of pity and hatred towards her then because she had recently acquired a bad reputation and I was thoroughly ashamed of her.

Li Xiaoyan, the deputy instructor, sat opposite with the blacksmith, Wang Zhigang, a sturdy man with a tanned, rough complexion, who gave the impression of being powerful, strong and determined. It seemed natural for us to compare him with Othello, and we had nicknamed him the "Moor". He liked to be alone, and had a just and ethical character. He didn't seek the limelight, and had a strong influence over the younger people. I rather envied him for that. It was the deputy instructor who had nominated him specifically to join our detachment. Now I stared with jealousy as Li rested her head on the Moor's broad shoulder to take a nap.

I asked myself why I was attracted to her. Was it her beauty? Certainly she was beautiful, a girl from Shanghai, with a lovely face, white, delicate skin, large, shining eyes, and thin, curved eye-brows. Her face always had an expression of wonder. Her slender figure seemed to confirm what we'd heard, that she had been a good ballet student in Shanghai and that many dance troupes had wanted to recruit her but that she'd refused them all. She had come to the Great Northern Wilderness of her own free will. From the first moment I saw her, I couldn't help being aware of her. But I wasn't usually one who was easily seduced or overwhelmed by pretty girls. On the contrary, whenever I meet a girl, the more beautiful she is, the more aloof I am. It's one of my maxims — never be a slave of love through indiscretion. Was it her seriousness, her solemnity that enticed me? Not really. I rather preferred girls with enthusiastic, frank and open-minded character. Sometimes I thought Li's solemn bearing was hypocritical and it disgusted me. It was true she'd sworn not to pay a home visit to Shanghai for three years in order to consolidate her determination to settle in that border area. She also made the suggestion that other girls in the company ought not to wear make-up or colourful clothes. But some of them passed it around that Li still worried about her white, delicate skin and that in summer she stealthily went to the river bank to get a suntan. Unfortunately the sunshine only turned her white skin pink, not the brown she wanted. She also tried to be more masculine, wearing what the boys wore, doing the same manual labour they did. She wanted to change her figure, to adopt the so-called "beauty of the labourer", but she remained slim and graceful. Strong and healthy, she was like a small white birch, erect and tall during those three years in the Great Northern Wilderness. She had not been home once during that time. In the first year she had become the head of the platoon, in the second a Party member, and the third the deputy instructor of the company, a model for the whole regiment, showing others how to strike roots in the frontier reclamation areas.

One summer evening in that third year, right after she was appointed deputy instructor of the company, I suddenly heard someone singing when I was sketching on the river bank.

Under the bright sky of early spring.
My eighteen-year-old lover sits on the river bank.
......

It was a "decadent" song strictly prohibited at the time. Who was singing it? If our deputy instructor heard about it, an "ideological struggle" would inevitably ensue. Whoever it was sang well. Her voice was very sweet. Burning with curiosity, I packed up my home-made drawing board and went quietly along the bank to find out who the singer was. Suddenly I came upon someone sitting on a large, smooth grey stone beneath a reclining willow tree on the opposite bank of the river. It was none other than our deputy instructor! She was washing her clothes, dangling her bare feet in the water, her trouser legs rolled up above the ankles and her white calves uncovered.

Under the bright sky of early spring,
My eighteen-year-old lover waits for her sweetheart,
Yinglian....

After scrubbing, kneading and wringing out the clothes, she stood up on the large grey stone and tiptoed cautiously across some pebbles to hang them over some branches. Afraid the pebbles might hurt her feet, she moved gingerly, with quick light steps, just like the dance of the cygnets in *Swan Lake*. Having spread the clothes across the shrubs, she returned to the river bank with the same steps. She collected a few wild flowers, taking in their scent and placing some in her hair, two on the right and three on the left. Then, squatting in front of the river, she stared for a long time at her own reflection in the water. She was admiring her own beauty! After a while she rose slowly. Then suddenly she jumped up on to the grey stone's smooth surface and, her arms outstretched, made an elegant semicircle and performed a Mexican folk dance with quick steps.

The drawing board slid from my hands and dropped into the water, causing a slight noise. Alarmed, she stopped dancing and saw me watching her from the opposite side of the river. She appeared stunned, like a bewildered fawn or a startled crane about to take flight.

The river between us, we stared at one another in astonishment.

The first to recover composure, I jumped into the river to retrieve my drawing board. Feigning a casual manner, I waded through the shallow water to the opposite bank. By then, the wild flowers in her hair had disappeared and the trouser legs had been rolled down.

"You ... what are you doing here on the river bank?" she asked, intending to gain the upper hand, and with it the psychological initiative. She tried her best to conceal her embarrassment, assuming a relaxed manner as much as she could. She became again a solemn, reserved young woman in the presence of a young man. A deputy instructor with the requisite dignity. But she hadn't had enough time to button up her jacket, faded from many washings, and underneath she wore a pink shirt, short and tight, with a V-neck through which I caught a glimpse of a white neck and bosom, round white shoulders and even the cleavage of her heaving breasts. Immediately I averted my eyes and felt my heart racing with excitement. I flushed, feeling an inexplicable kind of shame, guilty about debasing her and myself as well, though I could swear to heaven that I didn't, even for a moment, lust after her. I didn't even feel the instinctive response which ordinarily occurs when a young man meets an attractive girl, the passion which originated with Adam and Eve.

She was so very sensitive. As my eyes took her in, she immediately covered her jacket flap and turned round. When she turned back again I saw the old familiar deputy instructor, jacket buttoned right up, and feet burrowed deep into the sand to hide the fact that she had no shoes on.

I felt humiliated by her behaviour and tried to find words to break the awkward silence, but ended by blurting out something very foolish, "You're ... so beautiful!"

"What?" Her face blushed like a crimson cloud. My sudden appearance had caused her problems, placing her in an impossibly awkward position.

"What I ... I meant is that you danced beautifully. If I'm not mistaken, it was a Mexican folk dance, wasn't it?"

"Mexican dance? Don't make fun of me. I was just doing the radio limbering-up exercises for middle school students."

"Does that mean you're going to deny you were singing as well?"

"Singing a song? Why should I deny it? I did sing a song." In addition to her feigned puzzlement, she now added one more thing, an artificial directness. She began singing:

Near the Qinghe River, on Tigerhead Hill,
Is situated Dazhai production brigade

After singing two lines she said to me, "That's the song you heard me singing."

The blush had receded and she had completely recovered her normal complexion.

I felt that she had made a fool of me and treated me as though I was blind and deaf. I couldn't stand any more such insults. Suppressing my anger with great effort I said coldly, "No, that wasn't the song I heard. You sang: 'My eighteen-year-old lover waits for his sweetheart, Yinglian'!"

"'Eighteen-year-old lover?' 'His sweetheart Yinglian?' I've never even heard of such a song. Don't talk nonsense!'' She raised her slender eyebrows with a surprised and astonished expression, as if I had called her a thief.

So many hypocritical changes of expression had taken place on that lovely face.

I had nothing more to say, and just looked at her in astonishment. To me she looked like the Sphinx, with its lion's body and human face, only the Sphinx was more honest. As I remember, even the Sphinx said the same thing to everyone: If you fail to solve my riddle, then I will devour you. But the Sphinx was less shameless than this deputy instructor, since ultimately she jumped down from the rocks and died when Oedipus correctly answered the riddle. The deputy instructor wanted me, a normal person of sound mind, to believe myself to be an idiot, a daydreamer, talking in my sleep.

"You hypocrite!" Indignantly I turned around and abruptly strode off.

"Wait!"

I halted without turning around, but I could sense her anxiety.

"You ... are you going to report me to the company leader?..." she murmured, with an imploring tone.

Still with my back to her, I softened and shook my head. After walking a distance I could not help looking back. She remained standing beside the river like a statue, motionless....

I never told anyone else about the incident.

I couldn't be that mean.

But from then on, whenever she made her speeches she would become uneasy when our eyes met. I regretted that and felt sorry for her.

Not long after that I got a telegram saying that my mother was seriously ill, but I was unable to get permission from the company leader to return home. The reason was clear, since I was the combine harvester driver and it was then harvest season. Actually I knew that the company leader didn't believe the telegram was genuine. That was another reason he didn't approve my request. He had been deceived several times by phoney telegrams which parents or their children sent in order to arrange a reunion. Some of them even invented the death of a parent. As a consequence, the company leader had become an empiricist. It was no use pleading with him to let me go, nor would any kind of explanation help. But I couldn't remain indifferent to the telegram. My father had died early and my mother, a worker in a small factory, had brought up my younger sister and I through all kinds of difficulties and hardships. It had not been easy for her, and only I understood how she had put her heart and soul into looking after us. Now my younger sister and I had come to this Great Northern Wilderness and left her at home alone. She was a woman of strong character and would never use deceitful measures even though she was yearning to see us.

I decided I had to return immediately to see her.

That day I stealthily left the company....

My mother! This woman who had tasted to the full the bitterness of life! She was so unyielding, so concerned for her children. She knew she was dying but she only cabled us that she was "very sick" instead of "mortally ill". She didn't want to alarm us with such frightening words.

During my mother's last five days I lived with her

and gave her as much care and love as I could to thank her for bringing us into this world and helping us to grow up. I did this not only for myself but also for my younger sister who was unable to return.

Five days, only five days! No matter how I expressed my love or took care of my mother during those five days it was only a symbolic compensation. How can a mother's love and concern for her children ever be compensated?

My mother's last words were, "Look after your sister. You're all the family she has."

Numbed by grief, I went back to the company.

The day I returned, on the instruction of the company leader, the Youth League branch held a meeting to discuss what disciplinary action should be taken over my desertion. Before the meeting, someone had disclosed that I was certain to be expelled from the league. The meeting itself was purely a formality and I would be used as an example to warn the others.

I myself was totally indifferent to whatever punishment I had to have.

The meeting was conducted by the deputy instructor. I thought she would certainly use the opportunity to take her revenge and I was determined to keep my mouth shut and listen to her long criticism of me.

At first she asked me to say something about my mistake.

I looked down and muttered, "My mother ... died ... three days ago...." Finishing this sentence, I put my head in my hands and felt everyone's eyes focussed on me.

For an instant, it seemed that everyone at the meeting was holding their breath. Suffocated by the sudden silence, even the air seemed unnaturally still. Following this pause, the deputy instructor said in a low but clear voice, "The meeting is over...."

She was the first to leave.

As I passed by the company office, I heard the deputy instructor and the company leader arguing fiercely. I was surprised, since the deputy instructor was used to carrying out the company leader's instructions. Wondering what they were wrangling over, I stopped to listen.

"I am the head of this company. Don't I have the right to punish a subordinate?" It was the angry voice of the company leader with his heavy Sichuan accent.

"I am the Youth League branch secretary. Punishing League members is the duty of the League branch." The deputy instructor's voice was raised too.

"All you're doing is making excuses for a deserter!"

"A deserter? Did he desert the battlefield? Did he cross to the other side of the Heilong River? Do you know that his mother died? Three days after her death he came back...."

"Oh, his mother died, did she!?"

"Company leader, I am an educated youth too, with an elderly father and mother. They're longing to see me. I'd go back home this very minute if I hadn't taken an oath. But I can't. I don't agree that he should be expelled from the League. Company leader, please, put yourself in his position and think it over!"

I heard her start to cry. As I stood outside the company office, tears welled up in my eyes too.

I felt thoroughly grateful to her. Not because she
had defended me, but because she had said, "I am an
educated youth too...."

All of my misconceptions and prejudices about her
were erased by this sentence and I felt I would go
through hell for her.

Hearing this I knew she was a good person with a
noble character and a sympathetic heart. Nevertheless,
two days later this same person told me something
which hit me like a bolt of lightning.

That day, while helping me to turf out the weeds in
a long stretch of ground, she asked, "After work
would you mind coming with me?" It was the second
time in three years that she had talked to me. The first
had been the encounter by the river not long ago. This
time her sullen and serious expression seemed to omen
some misfortune.

As we shouldered our hoes and lined up to return,
she said to me in front of everyone else, "Please wait.
Let's go together." The others looked at both of us
with curious expressions.

After they had moved off a distance, she looked me
in the eye, and said, "Without consulting you, I've arranged to have your younger sister transferred to our
company."

"Why? What's happened? Tell me!"

"When you were home..."

"Tell me!"

"She had an abortion...."

Shocked I felt my body swaying and nearly fell.

She steadied me with her hands.

I roughly pushed her aside, shouting, "You're
lying!"

She staggered backward. Eyes wide with fear, she uttered two words, "It's true!"

I felt suddenly as if I was glued to the ground. I wanted to shout out but it was as if there was something stuffed down my throat and I couldn't. The only sound coming from my voice was a hoarse moan. My vision blurred and she became indistinct.

Like someone crazed, I raced towards the tent.

I wept through the whole of that night, biting the quilt corner to avoid disturbing my soundly sleeping roommates. I remembered my mother's last wish, but before I could carry it out, my younger sister had acted scandalously. Now she was to be transferred to my company so she could be under my wing. Never! With the right of an elder brother, I would punish her severely, on behalf of my dead mother.

The next day I was called to the office by the deputy instructor and there met my younger sister. On seeing her, I sprang at her like a leopard, took her hair and forcefully hit her head against the earthen wall.

"Stop!" I heard the deputy instructor's shout. She dashed forward trying hard to loosen my frenzied grip.

"Get away!" I roared at her.

I tormented my younger sister as though I was tormenting myself. My hysteria seemed to relieve the pain.

Suddenly, I received a sharp slap on the face.

I released my grip.

The second slap was much harder.

The two slaps had sobered me up and unconsciously I stepped back, feeling my burning cheek.

My younger sister didn't utter a single word, nor moan, shout or plead. Her dishevelled hair covered a pallid face bathed in tears, and her large eyes were full of humiliation.

Her face drained of colour, the deputy instructor held my younger sister tightly and stared at me, determined to fight if necessary.

"You bloody animal!"

That was the first time I ever heard her use bad language.

From that day on I was in love with her.

Now she was sitting opposite. As the covered, tractor-drawn sled slogged on through the whirling snow, we were chilled by the northwesterly wind. It carried snow-flakes into the tent through an open flap which no one wanted to draw. We looked at the white world out-side, the white land, the white mountains, the white river, the white forests. The blizzard violently pursued us, like millions of maddened galloping wild oxen.

After silently looking round at everyone, the deputy instructor then said, almost to herself, "Should we have someone tell a story? Or perhaps sing a song to-gether."

There was no response to her suggestion. Everyone was exhausted.

Her eyes fell on me.

I cleared my throat and began to sing *The Reclaimers' Song*:

Every reclaimer has a sun in his heart,
one hand holds a gun, the other a pickaxe.

No one joined in and so naturally I halted after the first two lines of the song.

Just then, Moor started to whistle. He wasn't a

good singer, but he could whistle quite tunefully. What surprised me though was that he was whistling the famous Russian folk song *Troika*. He wasn't at all afraid of the deputy instructor's interference. His whistling had an enchanting quality, like a clarinet or a trumpet. His lyrical, rhythmic melody produced in us a sense of sadness, of deep melancholy.

Someone started humming quietly, then another and a third, gradually converging into a chorus.

My younger sister looked up, stared uneasily and then, lowering her head again, heaved a long sigh. I felt sorry for her.

I gazed across at the deputy instructor's face, guessing that she would immediately put a stop to this sentimental song. But she remained indifferent. Her head was still resting on Moor's shoulder. Her eyes closed, she pretended to be falling asleep, but I noticed her hand covertly beating time.

I felt that my pride was somehow hurt and bit my lower lip. The song continued:

The Volga is covered with ice and snow,
The Troika is driving over the icy river.
Someone is singing a melancholy song,
The singer is ...

Night fell unobtrusively and the merciless blizzard stopped its howling. Maybe it surrendered itself or maybe, with our tractors driving at full throttle, we left it behind in that silent wilderness.

Now we were enclosed by the chill darkness, a huge natural tent flap.

2

Travelling like the migrant Oroqen people, we drove
swiftly across the vast snowy plateau for two days and
two nights. When we looked at the map, we were convinced that we had arrived at a snow-and-ice covered
Spirits' Swamp. A solemn dawn in the wilderness was
just breaking.

Spirits' Swamp! It was not as dreadful as the legends made out. Perhaps it was in hibernation and its
true ferocious appearance was hidden deep beneath the
snow. It seemed as if the largest lake in the world lay
frozen in front of us. Devil's Reach — it looked so
flat we could hardly believe that it extended only as far
as the remote horizon.

"Hey! Devil King, where are you? Show yourself!" shouted one of our companions.

But the "Devil" did not appear.

Suddenly Moor pointed to something in the distance, "Look!" A round wooden stake with a notch
cut into it stood at an angle.

Curious, we walked over to have a look. The deputy instructor brushed the snow from the stake and we
saw a wooden table with something carved on its
rough surface. Most of the words had been eroded by
wind and rain, but some poor handwriting was still
faintly visible: ... died here....

Each of us shuddered.

"There's another one over there!" My younger
sister had discovered a similar evil omen. She was the
first to walk back to the tractor.

The deputy instructor said softly, "Let's go back.
Don't disturb their rest."

If someone asks me what the hardest and bitterest work of all in the Great Northern Wilderness is, I'll answer "reclamation".

And if someone asks me what work in the Great Northern Wilderness I feel most proud of, my answer will. also be "reclamation".

Because we were eager to discover the best sources of water and timber, nearly every part of Devil's Reach was covered with our footprints. We finally discovered a stream —— not marked on the map —— which was the only clean water source. We named it the "Wanderer" since it had been wandering across the flat wasteland for countless years before we discovered it and set up a tent next to it.

When the snow melted, our gleaming ploughs sank into the bosom of Devil's Reach. Who but a reclaimer could experience the joy of ploughing the first plot of virgin land by tractor? There were many wolves on this flat land. In threes and fours they swaggered along behind the tractors, preying on field rats started by the ploughing and at night, they would howl around our tent. The hardship of this work had transformed all the young men in the detachment into saints. All of us, including my younger sister and the deputy instructor, lived in the same large tent. Their small "world" was separated from ours by a hanging blanket, behind which existed a sacred, forbidden place.

One night, I suddenly woke and could not hear the usual night shift tractor roaring outside the tent. I immediately sprang to my feet and, without thinking, barged into the "forbidden place" to shake the deputy instructor awake.

"What do you want?"

" Moor is out ploughing, but the tractor has stopped!''

With the tractor silent for such a long time, there must be something wrong with Moor. Everyone in the tent got up. Just as we were all about to run out, Moor suddenly appeared at the entrance, his hands gripping the two front paws of an old wolf which was clinging to his back. The animal was still half alive, its mouth wide open, its two back paws gripping either side of his waist.

"It's still alive! Quick! Hit it!'' shouted Moor.

We immediately took up sticks and clubs and beat the large grey animal to death.

Moor flung himself on a pallet gasping for breath. After a long pause he told us, "The steel cable on the big plough broke and I was changing it when that damned thing came at me and got me round the shoulders with its claws...." His face and hands were cut and bloodstained, his clothes in tatters. Frowning, he took off his padded jacket. His sweatshirt and skin had also been clawed.

The deputy instructor ordered my younger sister, "Quick, get the first-aid kit!''

Just then we suddenly realized that the deputy instructor, feet bare, was wearing only her underclothes. She had just become aware of it herself and felt uneasy at our stares. But she remained calm, and said coolly, "What are you looking at? Haven't you got anything better to do? Go to bed again, all of you!'' Submissively, one after another, people went to bed and buried themselves in their quilts once again. But I remained, holding the lantern above Moor's head.

It was the first time the deputy instructor had ever given me such a tender look. Without saying a word, she took the first-aid kit from my sister and carefully bandaged Moor's wounds....

My younger sister was the "minister of domestic affairs" of the detachment and did all our washing and cooking. All the frozen vegetables brought from the company had been eaten and no edible wild herbs could be found in such a cold winter, so she did her best to make different kinds of food for us with the remaining two bags of flour.

If I had joined this reclamation work because of the deputy instructor, then my younger sister had come to Devil's Reach because of me. I was her only family member. If I went to the ends of the earth she would go with me. Although I had treated her cruelly, she still wanted my protection and shelter. On the surface, I still appeared indifferent towards her, but in truth I had already wholeheartedly forgiven her.

Only those who are guilty of monstrous crimes do not forgive others. And after all, she was my younger sister, my only sister.

I was duty-bound to take care of her. Both before and after the scandal occurred, had I carried out my responsibilities as an elder brother? No, I hadn't. The first day we arrived in the Great Northern Wilderness, she had become fascinated by deer, and had asked if we could work at the deer farm together. But I had refused. I thought her fragility and wilfulness would cause me endless trouble and worry. Instead I had looked after my own affairs and shirked my duties as an elder brother. After her mistake, which had left her open to public censure, my first thought was that she had tarnished my reputation. I had detested her without feeling the slightest nights on Devil's Reach, I gradually realized my true nature. I had to confess to myself what a selfish brother, what a mean coward I was.

One day, when just the two of us were alone in the tent, I called over to her with a soft voice, "Sister!"

She was kneading flour on the chopping board. Hearing me calling, she raised her head and looked at me with a frightened expression, tears welling up in her eyes.

"Younger sister, are you still angry with me?" I moved to her side.

Tears, large tears trickled down her pallid face on to the dough she was kneading.

"Younger sister...." my voice was hoarse.

Turning around and throwing herself into my arms, she hugged me with flour-covered hands and sobbed.

After a long while she stopped. The first thing she asked me was, "Is Mum better?"

It was as though I had been stabbed in the heart.

Oh, Mother! If only you had heard what your daughter was saying, you would cry too.

May you not hear, and have no more worries about your children. But I wish that somehow you could know what your daughter had said, because she was the one who loved you most.

I hadn't the courage to tell my sister that our mother was dead. I worried about her delicate feelings and the fragile heart which wouldn't be able to bear such a shock.

I answered in a gentle voice, "She's not sick. She's been missing us terribly. When I told her that we were both all right, she felt better."

A wan smile appeared at the corners of her mouth, a pained and anguished smile. It was the first time she had smiled for several days.

"Tell me who the young man is. I want to teach him a lesson."

My sister firmly shook her head.

"Do you ... love ... him?"

Silent, she nodded.

"He.... How about him? Does he love you?"

Another silent nod.

I stared at her. The angelic expression on her face was obviously a reflection of her true feelings. I felt lost.

Suddenly she asked, "Elder brother, do you love her?"

"Who?"

"The deputy instructor!"

"Where have you heard such nonsense?"

"I discovered it for myself. She likes you a lot too."

"Really!?" I grabbed her tightly by the arm.

"Yes!"

"But she likes Moor!"

"She trusts him and so do I. He's worthy of our trust. Any girl would trust someone like him. But you're the one she's fond of. She told me that you have an artistic nature. She also knows that you're in love with her...." Suddenly she stopped talking.

Almost at the same time, both of us saw the deputy instructor standing by the entrance to the tent. She had obviously overheard our conversation.

"Aiya! I must go and collect the clothes I left drying by the river." Finding an excuse, I fled from the tent, racing wildly across the flat land. Devil's Reach seemed to be the most beautiful place in the whole world.

That day after eating our evening meal, we all gathered together in the tent to tell stories, something we did quite often to amuse ourselves. We told all sorts of stories: fairy stories, ghost stories, horror stories, humorous stories.... Each of us, including the deputy instructor, freed of the company's fetters, seemed to have come into our own in Devil's Reach.

The deputy instructor told us a tale from the *Odyssey*, of how the great Odysseus, returning to his homeland of Ithaca after attacking Troy, was detained by a headwind in an isolated island with his companions. She told us how the residents of the island presented them with a magic plant, common on the island, which was so delicious that upon eating it a person would forget all of their troubles. Odysseus and his companions forgot their homeland, their parents, their brothers, sisters, wives and friends after eating this plant and so they stayed on the island for the rest of their days....

To my surprise, the deputy instructor told this story in such a natural, unexaggerated manner that we were all moved by the depth of feeling she expressed.

She finished her story and left us all deep in thought. Only my younger sister heaved a long sigh, and said to herself, "I'd like to get a lot of those magic plants."

The deputy instructor sat next to Moor, her head resting against his shoulder as usual. The flames from the big stove cast a red glow across her face. As the light flickered over her pretty features, an expression of longing and sadness appeared before my eyes.

I inevitably felt a deep sympathy for her. Had she not been restrained by the oath she had made three years earlier, she could have visited her family. Three years! She must have missed her parents and friends more than any of us.

I opened my board and said, "Don't move, Moor, I want to draw both of you." Actually I really only wanted to draw the deputy instructor, so beautiful she was, but I dared not openly say so. However, Moor thought that I was publicly mocking him, something he could not endure. It was obvious that he had misunderstood.

When the deputy instructor subconsciously moved her head away from his shoulder, he clutched her hand and stared at me coldly, "Don't move! Let him draw. Don't disappoint him!" There was a hint of challenge in his intonation. The deputy instructor obediently leaned her head against his shoulder again and looked at me with a faint smile.

Without saying anything more I began to sketch. I was determined that the drawing would be meticulous, would really convey her beauty. So I looked up at her and drew several strokes, took another look, and drew several more. Never had I worked so carefully on a sketch. Finally I finished it and intentionally broke my pencil lead on the very last stroke.

"I'm sorry, I haven't done it very well." I handed it over to the deputy instructor.

Everyone gathered around admiring the sketch.

"Not bad! It looks just like her!"

"Ah! That's really quite a talent you've got. Why have you kept it a secret from us? Will you draw me one day?"

"*Aiya*, you've only drawn me!" The deputy instructor threw a glance at Moor.

"I'm sorry. My pencil broke." I flushed slightly.

The deputy instructor took the sketch and looked at it carefully for a while and then said, "May I have it?"

"Certainly. You can keep it if you like."

"I'll look after it." She looked down. As she did, Moor stood up and slipped out of the tent. From that day on he was much more reticent.

Everything in life can be passed on except love.

I would persist in my pursuit of her, never give up my love for her, never love another, never....

The first spring rain came.

The soil of the reclamation fields, dark and rich, was like a baby greedily sucking Mother Nature's milk. People often compare spring to a gorgeously dressed young maiden, but it was travelling over Devil's Reach more like a solemn woman, walking slowly and with measured paces. Carrying her uniquely gentle dye with her, she turned the world green.

One day the deputy instructor fainted by the banks of the Wanderer. She was ill and did not come to for two days. While in a coma, she kept mumbling, "Wheat seeds, wheat seeds." None of the medicines in our first-aid kit could reduce her temperature. On the third day she came to, called my sister to her bedside, and asked, "How much food is left now?"

"Only a little," answered my sister.

The deputy instructor looked about with an expression of deep concern, and said with a smile, "My dear friends, on behalf of the company I want to thank all of you. I am going to suggest that the Party branch record your merits. Now, except for one or two of us, everyone should return to the company and give them a hand moving here. This must be finished before the ice on Spirits' Swamp melts!'' She gently took my sister's hand, "You have to stay with me, otherwise I'll feel lonely.''

"I want to.''

"I'll stay too,'' I said.

Moor looked over at the deputy instructor, "I'd like to stay as well, if you agree.''

She nodded her approval.

Now only the four of us remained on Devil's Reach.

One day, a second ... four days passed. The company still had not arrived. A company of more than two hundred people on the move would inevitably mean many difficulties. But, within those four days, Spirits' Swamp had completely melted. Our trusted friend, the Wanderer River had betrayed us and collaborated against us with the Spirits' Swamp. When my sister and I went out on the fourth day, we were stunned by the change in the environment: in one night, the clear, meandering Wanderer had become a rushing current, turbid and muddy, like a wild galloping horse with hairpin turns and whirlpools, lumps of snow and ice, withered branches and broken trees. The river had overflowed and poured water across the swamp. Spirits' Swamp was now a vast expanse of water.

My sister was worried, "If the company doesn't arrive today, we won't have anything to eat.''

Moor and I shot her a glance but said nothing. What we were most worried about was how the company would cross the swamp.

Without saying anything more, my sister went back into the tent, and Moor and I followed. She sat on a pallet beside the deputy instructor, who was still in a coma, and tears filled her eyes. Catching sight of us, she quickly wiped them away, picked up a sickle and a small basket and said, "I'm going out to dig some wild herbs."

It was almost noon when suddenly we heard my sister calling out from a distance, "Brother, brother, quick, come here!"

Moor and I immediately jumped to our feet and ran out of the tent where we saw my sister, like a small terrier, chasing after a weak roe deer. Tossing her sickle, she hit its rear leg and it fell. She sprang at it, but failed to hold it. Struggling free, the deer ran towards the swamp. My younger sister was on its heels. At the edge of the swamp it stopped for a moment as if looking back at her, then jumped and fled, limping.

"Stop!"

"Sister!"

Moor and I shouted at her.

My younger sister was at the very edge of the swamp, pacing up and down. She finally came to a halt and looked at the deer with its mired feet. After a slight hesitation, she made a first cautious step into the Spirits' Swamp.

"Come back! It's dangerous...." shouted Moor as we ran towards her.

My younger sister turned round to look at us and then waved her hand as if to say, "Leave me alone...."

When Moor and I reached the edge of the swamp, she had already caught the deer. Struggling with the small animal, she suddenly sank deep into the mire. Before we could even think what to do, all we could see was her small hand repeatedly grasping the air. In an instant, both my sister and the deer had completely disappeared from sight.

"Keep away...." Her last words in this world still echo in my ears.

"Sister——" I shouted and darted recklessly at the swamp.

With his strong arms Moor grabbed me from behind. I struggled against him and then lost consciousness.

When I recovered I found myself lying in the tent, the image of my younger sister's tiny hand appearing repeatedly before my eyes. My mother's last wish rang again in my ears and tears welled up. I struggled to get up and saw Moor standing still outside the tent. His tall figure was silhouetted clearly against the pale moon. The eerie song of a bird rang out over the swamp and sent cold shivers down my spine. Perhaps the bird was calling back my younger sister's soul. I wasn't superstitious, but the thought suddenly flashed across my mind. I stared at Moor and blazed with hatred towards him. Had he not restrained me, I believed I would certainly have been able to save my younger sister. I was consumed with guilt over her death.

I stood up and staggered out of the tent. When Moor heard my footsteps, he turned slowly round, his eyes wide open, and stared at me in astonishment. Maybe he knew I was enraged, for he instinctively stepped back.

I abruptly raised my fist.

"You —— " Stunned, he stepped back again.

"I hate you!" I growled, clenching my teeth.

He fixed his eyes on me and said in a low, deep voice, "If it's because of your sister, then I have the right to defend myself. Do you think I have the heart of a devil? Don't you think I'm upset about your sister's death? If I could change places with her, I'd willingly be caught in that swamp myself. If it's because of her...." he threw a glance at the tent, "then go ahead and hit me! So long as I'm still alive, and she's not your wife, I have the right to love her."

His words made me shiver. As though paying condolences to my younger sister, I lowered my head. A silence reigned over the night. The flat wilderness was quiet and sullen, and even the song of the eerie bird who called back lost souls had died away.

Moor slowly turned and walked away into the darkness. Soon his figure was lost in the hollow black night.

"What are you two quarrelling about?"

I looked over my shoulder to see the deputy instructor standing by the tent. In the past four days she had become so weak that, had she let go of her grip on the tent flap, she would most certainly have collapsed.

After a long silence two words fell from my lips, "The wolf ..."

"Wolf?..." Scrutinizing my expression, she asked, "You're hiding something from me. Where's Moor? Where is your sister? Where have they gone? Tell me! What's happened?"

"My sister ... died in the swamp...." I couldn't hold back my sorrow any longer and covered my face with my hands, sobbing aloud.

On hearing this, she uttered only a short "Oh!"

and fainted, as if she'd suddenly received a heavy blow.

Moor had not returned even though it was now deep into the night. Where could he have gone? Would he come back and share the same tent with me again? Had he met with some mishap? If he had any kind of accident I would be responsible....

I was plunged into confusion, and waited anxiously for his safe return, feeling the dark night move on its long course. I took care of the still-unconscious deputy instructor. It was the first time in the unlimited vastness of that flat wilderness that I experienced such dreadful loneliness. The whole night long I could not fall asleep.

At dawn I heard the hurried clatter of hoofs in the distance and ran out of the tent to find Moor dismounting from a horse.

"Where did you get the horse?" I said in a friendly manner, trying to put aside all of the unpleasantness between us.

"Several days ago, I found a branch with a trail marker cut into it and knew there must be some Oroqen hunters nearby. I found them yesterday and borrowed it from them. How is the deputy instructor?"

"Still unconscious."

"The Oroqen hunters told me that maybe she has haemorrhagic fever."

"Haemorrhagic fever?!" I froze. I had once heard of someone dying of that like a leaf ripped down by the autumn wind.

"Take this horse and escort the deputy instructor back to the company right now," ordered Moor. "You must go back the way we came and you will probably meet up with our company and be able to save her.''

"No, I'll stay here and you take her.''

"I'm too heavy. If I try and take her, the horse will certainly collapse halfway there. It's already exhausted. The two of you go together. If you head westward fifty *li* you can cut around Spirits' Swamp, and go due west beside it!''

To continue arguing with him would have been hypocritical.

Moor tied the unconscious deputy instructor to my back and then helped me mount.

"Take the gun!''

"You keep it.''

"No, you should take it. You need to be prepared for any eventuality.'' He fastened the gun to the saddle, reined the horse around and then, gave the animal a strong punch on its rump.

The horse neighed, and raced westward at full gallop.

Although the westward route was thirty *li* less than the eastward one, we had to cross a vast grassland. We were fortunate in having a well-bred Oroqen hunter, a short and compact animal, not handsome but able to bear hardships and stand up to gruelling work. It really is the hunters' friend, the camel of the wilderness.

Having passed the Spirits' Swamp I continued urging the horse on. It seemed to understand what I wanted, and galloped on without slackening. After travelling nearly thirty *li* I felt my cotton-padded trousers drenched by the animal's sweat. Suddenly it snorted several times and began to stagger. It tried to continue with all its strength, but its forelegs buckled.

As soon as I dismounted, it instantly inclined to one side, stretched out its neck, and collapsed.

The horse's belly rose and fell, warm air spurting from its nostrils, its mouth dribbling white foam. Before lying down, the intelligent animal had paused to prevent its full weight crushing down on its rider's leg and had looked at me almost apologetically with its clear eyes.

"Put me down! Put me down! Where are we? What are we doing here? Where are you taking me?"

The deputy instructor had come to, and struggled against the rope tying her to me.

I untied the rope and gently put her down on the ground, her head and shoulders leaning against my chest.

"I'm taking you to meet the company. You're seriously ill."

She murmured, "Am I going to die? Is that it?"

I felt upset hearing my beloved say such words and replied in a loud voice, "No, of course not!"

She forced a smile, "I'm not afraid of death. Really. Don't you remember the lines in our oath to settle in the wilderness: 'It's not necessary to be buried on our home village, everywhere in the wilderness is our home.' The only thing I regret is that in a few months I would have been able to visit my parents. I really miss them. They're longing for my visit, nearly going crazy over it. I've written them a letter promising to go after the autumn harvest here, but now...."

I sobbed, my tears falling on her face.

"Don't cry." She gently took my hand. "If I do die, please bury me beside Spirits' Swamp and let me keep your younger sister company. She was a good girl. My only request is that on my grave tablet, I would like the word 'reclaimer' carved together with my name...." Large tears gradually filled the corners of her eyes.

I held her tightly and sobbed loudly and bitterly.

"Look, what's that? It's like that magic fruit in the legend. Would you break off a branch for me, please?" Her large, beautiful eyes were fixed on something nearby.

Following her line of vision, I saw a cluster of purplish-red azaleas in bud. I helped her to lean against the saddle and went over to break off the branch. She was dead when I returned with the blossoms.

She and the Oroqen horse had stopped breathing at the same time.

Beneath me I felt the ground spinning; above, the blue sky turned black.

Wiping my eyes and pinning the azaleas to her chest, I knelt down and kissed her pale lips for a long time. I think that had she been alive, she would not have blamed me.

Carrying her body on my back, I walked on.

I saw the company expressed sorrow at the death of the deputy instructor. Each and everyone cried.

......

When the company caravan, the carts, sleds, tractors and trucks drew near the swamp, it was already dusk. Someone found a cotton-padded hat stuck on a wooden pole temporarily used as a grave marker. I went ahead and removed the hat. It was Moor's dog-skin hat. A slip of paper inside read: "I've discovered a way through Spirits' Swamp and have marked it with twigs. A *li* east of here...."

That night the whole company passed safely across the swamp leaving behind only the carts which might get stuck. But nowhere could we find Moor.

The next morning, beside the Wanderer we discovered bloody strips of Moor's clothing, a big axe and three dead wolves.... There had been a fierce fight between him and the wolves. We imagined how he had fallen after having fought with all his might against them.

During those sorrowful days we began to seed Devil's Reach.

In accordance with her last wishes, we buried the deputy instructor by the Spirits' Swamp. From Camel Mountain, a hundred miles away, we transported a huge grey stone which the old mason in our company chiselled into a grave tablet and on which he carved the words: In memory of reclaimers Li Xiaoyan, Wang Zhigang, Liang Shanshan, our beloved comrades....

On Camel Mountain we felled more than a thousand pine trees to make a road across Spirits' Swamp along the markers placed by Moor, and named it "Reclaimers' Road". The following years several other companies came to settle on the Devil's Reach.

At last we conquered Spirits' Swamp.

One silent dusk when I visited the reclaimers' graves I saw a stranger standing there and found a bunch of azaleas on the tablet. Azaleas had been my sister's favourite flower.

In an instant, I understood that the stranger was the young man who had been in love with her.

From the expression on his face, I could see that he would never leave Devil's Reach.

We exchanged a glance and he turned and walked slowly away.

I didn't stop him to ask his name, nor even think to ask where he came from....

He was one of our generation —— that was all I needed to know.

We had experienced the blizzards of the Great Northern Wilderness, the hardships and the joy of reclaiming this land of wonder and mystery. From then on, no matter what the difficulties were, whether we stayed or whether we left nothing could produce fear in us, nor make us surrender.... The Great Northern Wilderness!

Translated by Shen Zhen

Father

I want to set down on paper this piece of factual writing about my father — a worker, originally of peasant stock — to glorify him in a permanent way and to preserve in a son's memory something that he can offer to his own son in the future....

When I was very young, Father was, in my eyes, the severe master of our household, the unquestionable authority of the family, my supporter through his manual labour, my benefactor, and the source of my fear.

If Father put on a stern expression, my mother and the four of us sons would feel uneasy, like birds interacting with an impending thunderstorm.

Very seldom did Father feel happy or look cheerful.

At that time my younger sister was not yet born and my grandfather still alive. He lay in bed coughing away the whole day long, too old to move a step of his own accord but still keeping up a good appetite. The big family of seven with their efficient digestive systems were all catered for by the sweat of the brow of this third-grade plasterer. In Mother's words, the whole family was "eating" Father every day.

Father was an unyielding man from Shandong Province. He never complained about life nor sighed in despair. With a stern face, he let us freely "eat" him. His motto in life was: In everything rely on no-one but yourself. Our neighbours observed that our family "has a doorway on the roof and a well within the room" —— that we had no dealings with others.

I used to pray that Father would grumble over something or sigh from time to time. Once I heard an old woman in the neighbourhood who knew about fortune-telling say: "Everyone has a breath of qi* in his chest." Naively I believed that Father would flare up less if he sighed more.

But Father just wouldn't sigh.

It had been decided by his "fate", I guessed. What a misfortune! I felt sorry for Father and for the whole family, too. Whenever Father lost his temper, I felt it was easy to understand, even sympathize with him. A man couldn't do anything about his own "fate", neither could others. What was more, we were "eating" Father day by day. Couldn't we tolerate such a man occasionally losing his temper with his "eaters"?

The first time Father lost his temper with me left me with a lifelong impression. A big boy who was fond of bullying his inferiors had ripped two slits in the back of my brand-new jacket with a broken piece of glass. Without giving me a chance to explain, Father slapped me hard in the face. I did not cry, for I didn't dare to, but I felt terribly wronged. For the next three days I was silent. However, family life did not appear unusual in the slightest just because one of the four children said nothing for three days. No one in the

*One of the literal meanings of qi is "breath" or "air". In traditional Chinese medical theory and philosophy, it means "vital energy" or "energy of life".

family even noticed.

On the fourth day, in class, my teacher called me to stand up and read aloud a text. The text was very familiar as I had read it aloud time and time again. I did not open my mouth for a long time after I had stood up. The teacher became anxious, so did my classmates. They all stared at me anxiously as a row of seven or eight teachers from another school were sitting in the back of the classroom, watching.

It was not that I did not want to read the text and make my class lose face but I just couldn't find my voice. I was simply unable to utter the very first character of the text. I was even more anxious than either my teacher or my classmates.

"What's wrong with you? Why don't you start reading?" The teacher flushed with anger.

I burst out crying.

From then on, teacher's pet, the model of text reader disappeared from Class Three, Grade Two of the primary school and in his place emerged a "stammerer". From then on, my self-esteem was painfully lost....

My stammer was not corrected until after I went to high school when I corrected it myself. Nevertheless, I became a man slow of speech. Because of this, some assumed I was very "mature", others "shrewd" or "subtle". However, when it was necessary for me to "argue strongly on just grounds", I often stammered or fell silent again as if finding myself bested in argument. Father never offered me an apology for he never dreamed of associating that slap of his with my stammer....

Grandfather was also extremely irascible. When Father lost his temper, we would be happy if Grandfather did not follow suit.

Few were the occasions when we could feel happy, though.

Mother was born in the year of the sheep. She was as docile as a lamb, absolutely ruled by Father. Had their positions been the other way round, I believe it might have been more beneficial for us children. The daughter of a private villageschool teacher, Mother was fairly literate.

The women of poor families in China, their adaptability and their endurance to straitened circumstances in life are much to be admired. By instinct they cherish hopes for a bright future, though those hopes may be obscure, unrealistic and tinged with romantic notions. The expectation that their children might grow up to be successful adults serves as a breeding ground for those hopes. My mother's consciousness and confidence in that respect is, I think, stronger than most other mothers'.

With regard to "promise of success", Father had his own understanding.

One day during a meal, I was about to help myself to a second bowl of corn gruel when I noticed Father staring at me. Discouraged, I stopped before the gruel pot hesitantly, not daring to take more.

But Father encouraged me: "Go on! Have another bowlful!"

Seeing that I only ladled in half a bowl, he added: "Fill it up!" Then pointing at my elder brother and two younger brothers with his chopsticks, Father continued with an unusual solemnity, "You should all be able to eat a lot. It's only in this way that you will gain physical strength. At present you are living off my muscles, but in the future you'll have to depend on your own strength!''

For the first time, I perceived in his face a look of sincere kindness, of heart-felt joy, of ardent expectations, radiance and love.

I gobbled up that brimming bowl of gruel and forced down half a piece of steamed cornbread as well in order to repay Father for that rare flash of kindness and nobility he had shown us. Although my stomach was fit to burst, I felt happy. For the first time I had experienced paternal love. My heart was deeply touched by that precious experience.

With a schoolchild's comprehension, I looked to those words of Father's for guidance: an overwhelming principle, an unquestionable piece of advice with himself as a convincing example. I understood his advice and reverently followed his guidance. From that day on, my appetite increased and so did my strength, it seemed. I felt as if I was getting more and more muscular by the day.

"Each of those Liang children looks like a wolf cub. Just look how voraciously they gobble up the corn bread, corn gruel and pickles at each meal. It just makes your mouth water!'' That was the only thing our neighbours envied us for. Father was proud of us.

When I was ten, Father went away to the northwest with a construction company to assist in the development of that region. Shortly after his departure, my grandfather died. Later on, my younger sister was born. Then Mother fell ill. Because of her illness, she was unable to breast-feed Younger Sister. Elder Brother, already a high school student, prepared medi-

cinal herbs for Mother each day and organised the rest
of the family members to keep things going. Every day
I fetched milk for Younger Sister and bottle-fed her
under Mother's instructions.

I had been longing for an elder sister. Mother had
given birth to a girl before me. But I don't know
what she looked like for she died when she was not yet
three. Bad luck caused her to die young. Father did
not believe in Western medicine so he would not allow
Mother to take the sick child to such a hospital for
treatment. When Mother succeeded in doing so without Father's knowledge, the doctor said it was too
late. Mother collapsed after Elder Sister's death. Yet
Father never thought he was in any way responsible.
In his opinion, Elder Sister had definitely been pois-
oned by those two tablets of Western medicine.

"Western medicine, that's for treating foreigners.
Their inner constitution is different from that of us
Chinese. How can we count on Western medicine for
the cure of a Chinese person's disease? If Western medi-
cine could do it, what did our Chinese ancestors invent
Chinese medicine for?!" he roared at Mother.

"It was the traditional Chinese medicine doctor who
asked me to take the child to a doctor trained in Western medicine," retorted Mother.

"He who said that is certainly not a good doctor of
Chinese medicine!" Father was even more vexed.

Mother could do nothing but shed silent tears.

The old woman in our neighbourhood who knew
about fortune-telling once said that *yang** was much

---

*In China's Taoist philosophy and traditional Chinese medicine,
yin is the feminine or negative principle in nature or man while
yang is the masculine or positive principle.

stronger than *yin* in our family so that girl children couldn't possibly survive, that Father was too strong and rigid by nature so no girls dared to be born into our family, and that Elder Sister had been "pressed" away by the *yang* or masculinity in our family to be reborn in another.

As a young child, I believed in such superstitious practices as fortune-telling. Otherwise, why had Younger Sister been born after Father's departure and Grandfather's death, not before? I looked after her whole-heartedly, hoping that she would be a brave girl and that Father would stay away from home for three years. I was afraid that she too would be "pressed" away to another family as Elder Sister had been. To a certain extent, Younger Sister's arrival was a compensation which satisfied my longing for an elder sister.

As I wished, Father did not return to visit us for three years, not for fear that he might "press" Younger Sister away but because he wanted to save up some money.

Although far away from home, Father tried to control his family with his principle in life: In everything rely on no one but yourself.

"Be thrifty. Count every fen and make every fen count. Don't, whatever you do, borrow money here or ask for a loan there...." In every letter home which he asked others to write for him, Father never forgot to earnestly exhort Mother against borrowing. The sum of money he sent home monthly was not enough to cover the essential expenses of the family and Mother totally betrayed Father's principle. Our family's "self-reliance" phase sadly came to an end. Poverty even deprived us of our psychological pride....

Father's first visit home was just before one Chinese New Year. He had saved up over three hundred yuan. Little more than a hundred was left after paying the debts raised by Mother.

"How have you been handling the finances? Huh? I urged you over and over again in my letters and in spite of this you still borrowed so much. How can I possibly support you all if you lead such a life?" Father roared at Mother in our presence. He sat on the edge of the *kang*, roaring and hitting it with his large callused hand.

Mother just listened silently.

"Dad, scold us instead if you want to. But we haven't spent one fen unnecessarily." Elder Brother indignantly tried to defend Mother.

Holding my schoolbag I went over to Father and emptied out its contents onto the *kang*. Among them were exercise-books fully used on both sides and a few pencil stubs about the length of a finger. Staring at Father, I silently declared that we really hadn't spent one fen extravagantly.

"What are you doing? How can you stand there as thoughtlessly as a small child?" Mother rebuked us sternly.

Turning his face away, Father dropped his head and stopped roaring. A long moment passed before he heaved a deep sigh. It sounded like the sigh from the heart of a discouraged man bearing a heavy burden.

That was the first time I had ever heard Father sigh.

All at once, I felt a kind of pity for him.

The next day, Father took us all to a department store. He bought clothes for each of us and a velvet jacket for Mother as well....

Father's second home-leave was during China's three-year natural calamity period in the '60s.

"I was wrong! I was totally wrong!..." Father examined his children one by one, whose faces were the colour of famine and terribly swollen from eating wild herbs.

"What do you mean 'You're wrong'?" Mother asked cautiously.

Father rumbled in reply, "Maybe I shouldn't have made that journey to the Northeast to eke out an existence when I was twelve.... I think maybe it's easier to live in my native place than in a city. Seeing as we have to live on wild herbs, we might as well try where there are more edible ones...."

Father wanted to go and take a look at his old home. If life was really easier there than in the city, he would take Mother and the five children back to the countryside. He would abandon his present job as a construction worker and become a farmer again.

The idea made us children excited and filled our hearts with hope. We were not infatuated with the city. Where there were safe things to fill up our stomachs, whether wild herbs or leaves, that would be home. Father's words kindled our longing for the hometown we had never been to.

Mother objected though. But once Father had decided to do something, he would insist on doing it. It was impossible to dissuade him.

Mother had never succeeded in altering any of Father's ideas, not even the most ridiculous one. She did not possess any such feminine skills and she knew it. So she started to make preparations for the journey.

Father decided that he would take one son with him.

That decision set the four of us quarrelling. In the end, Father clinched the matter.

Solemnly, he announced, "Second Son, I will take you to Shandong with me."

That visit to our native village left a dreary impression on me. It completely shattered my hopes; to Father, it was a psychological and emotional blow. Father no longer had any kin there but nevertheless that was where his old home had been. The locals greatly admired Father for his wages in cash, whereas the children greatly admired me for being a city boy and for the pair of brand-new rubber-soled shoes I wore. The wild herbs there were hardly enough to fill up their stomachs. In their eyes, the steamed bread left over from our journey was like high-quality pastry. Affected by the atmosphere of hunger in the village, Father and I just pretended we had made good.

Of the three hundred yuan or so Father had scraped up for his second visit home, almost nothing was left. Besides our fares, most of the money was given away in small sums to the villagers. Father and I left with a small pack of shelled peanuts and some dried sweet-potato slices presented by the villagers....

On our arrival home, the first thing Father said to Mother was, "Mum, I've squandered all our savings! Don't get angry, though. I'll save up again!..."

That was the first time I heard Father speak to Mother in such a tone.

Mother smiled lightly: "Why should I? Ever since you left your native village, you never went back to pay a visit. It goes without saying that's what you ought to have done." She sounded as if she did not mind at all that over three hundred yuan had been used up.

But I knew she did really. When she turned away, I saw tears spill over from the corners of her eyes and wet her jacket.

That night, Father tossed and turned in bed sighing endlessly.

Two days later, Father returned to the Northwest ahead of schedule. Working during a holiday was paid double....

2

Father scrupulously abided by the unalterable rule he had laid down for himself till his retirement: visit home once every three years. Father was good at saving while Mother was good at making ends meet by borrowing. Our family needed exactly that combination of such a father and such a mother.

In the photographic plate of my memory, Father became an increasingly blurred figure, the negative of which was developed only once every three years. In my heart, he became more and more a benefactor whom I wanted to repay, yet was unable to.

In a father-son relationship, that feeling of debt is, in essence, a dilutant that thins the feelings of kinship between flesh and blood. In its mild form twists the most normal of human feelings and the most justified moral principles into the most absurd sense of obligation. Poverty is a curse because it results in debts both spiritual and material.

The year of Father's third visit home fell in the

same year that Elder Brother was to take the university entrance examination. As head of the family, Father strongly opposed Elder Brother's desire to go to university.

"I can't afford to send you to university!" His words made Mother and Elder Brother feel there was no room for discussion.

A sympathetic neighbour found a temporary job for Elder Brother to earn a small amount of money: selling vegetables in a market. Every ten *jin** of vegetable would fetch five fen. Father forced Elder Brother to earn this tiny sum of money. Elder Brother would leave home early and return late, hiding a textbook in his clothes. Back home he would hand Father fifty fen which Mother had secretly given him earlier. Actually he had been to a park or the bank of the Songhua River to review his lessons. In the end the whole pretence was exposed. Father flew into a rage at the "schemes and intrigues" and smashed our mirror with a glass.

Father was so angry that he decided to go back to the Northwest that very day. Elder Brother and I went to see him off at the station.

Just before the train was due to leave, Father leaned out of the carriage window and said to Elder Brother, "Eldest Son, do follow my advice. Don't go to university. In our family of seven, it's only me who is earning a living. I'm already over fifty now. My health is becoming infirm with age. It's time you shouldered part of the load for me!..." One could sense his immeasurable pain and the piteous imploring in his voice.

---

*A unit of weight used in China equal to 500 grams.

When the train began to pull out, Father shed tears. One drop hung on the black bristles on his unshaven cheek. I felt miserable, unable to tell whether it was for Father or for Elder Brother. I knew that Elder Brother had taken the entrance examination without Father's knowledge. Mother had deceived Father once more; so had Elder Brother. I, who was in the know but had helped to conceal the fact from Father, had also deceived him. I felt terribly guilty. I realized that, to a great extent, I was miserable for myself....

A few days later, Elder Brother received an admission notice from the university. Mother smiled a gratified smile but Elder Brother cried over it....

I went to the station to see Elder Brother off. But he would not let me see him to the platform.

"Spare the five fen for a platform ticket." he said. At the ticket barrier, Elder Brother spoke to me again, "Second Brother, I trust you to help support the family in the future! Please don't tell Father that I'm going to university...."

Standing woodenly outside the entrance, I watched him follow the stream of people into the station. He kept looking back, a roll of bedding in his left hand and a string bag in the right.

Slowly I walked home, grasping tight the spared five-fen coin. I said to myself: The whole family should save every coin and make it go even further, for Elder Brother, for the first university student of our family for generations....

There was no way to hold back from Father for long the fact that Elder Brother had gone to university. I had to reveal the truth in a letter to him.

Elder Brother was sent back home in his first vacation.

He was unable to continue studying.

He was later taken to a mentaling hospital __ a free kingdom in the spiritual world; a lifelong home for the psychologically weak; for him a clear and definite end.

Looking through Elder Brother's diary, I found in between the leaves a letter from Father, a letter in which more than half of the characters were wrongly written, revealing his half illiteracy:

> Eldest Son! You are too selfish! You don't have your parents in your heart! Nor your brothers and sister! All you think of is yourself! Go ahead for a bright prospect whole-heartedly! As if I've brought you up for nothing! As if you are no longer my son! Even if you become an engineer one day I will not take you for my son again!

Every sentence was followed by an exclamation mark. It seemed that even they failed to fully express Father's wrath over Elder Brother. Reflecting on it now, the incident was extremely lamentable, for both Father and for Elder Brother.

I went to the Great Northern Wilderness before Father's fourth visit home. I did not see him for another seven years. I could not, as I wished, visit home at the same time as Father.

In my seventh year there, I was admitted to Fudan University in Shanghai.

Before the admission notice reached me, I was laden with anxiety. After several sleepless nights, I wrote Father a letter, asking him for a remittance of two hundred yuan. I also told him in the letter that it was my last chance to go to university because I was already twenty-five. As soon as the letter was dropped into the postbox I was sorry. But it was too late. I guessed that Father would either simply not reply or write to give me a vigorous scolding. In all events, it would be more ruthlessly written than the one to Elder Brother.

To my surprise, Father immediately remitted the sum, exactly two hundred yuan. By telegraphic transfer. Under Remitter's Message on the money order were a few wrong characters written in a very poor hand: "Not enuf, let me no."

I collected the remittance on that same day. It was drizzling that evening. I placed the bank notes separately in two pockets, one hundred in each, and put both hands in my pockets too, tightly grasping the two wads till they were damp.

I walked in the drizzle, slowly. A voice full of sympathy sounded in my ear, "It is really hard for Old Master Liang to support such a big family all by himself! He is very, very thrifty. A single cube of preserved beancurd is divided up to last for three meals. He even begrudges a dish of stir-fry...."

Those were the words spoken to Mother by one of Father's fellow workers when he called on us. I was a little boy then. Many things were forgotten as I grew up, but those words stayed fast in my memory. I felt the two wads of notes become heavy in my pockets as if they were two huge pieces of lead.

I strolled far away from our encampment. Hiding myself in between two piles of timber, I wept uncontrollably. I wept for myself and for Father, too. Why hadn't he written to abuse me?!

The next day we carried logs. I insisted on swapping from the third lever to the second, a position with the heaviest load. When eight men led by one of us chanting the work song, heaved up the huge ten-ton log, in my heart I echoed a different song. No, Dad! I won't!...

That dark drizzling night will remain in my memory for ever....

3

During the three years I spent in university, to save money on a half-price student concession train ticket from Shanghai to Harbin, I did not go home even once to visit my family. I hoped that every month Father would have one cube of preserved beancurd less and one dish of stir-fry more.

I did not return to visit them until I had worked a full year after graduation. I had not set eyes on Father for ten whole years. He retired earlier than expected. Once he fell off some scaffolding and suffered internal injuries. Besides, he was getting old, no longer capable of doing heavy physical work.

Arriving home, I saw Third Brother lying in bed with one leg in splints suspended in the air. Younger Sister told me that he was going to get married. The bridal chamber was a lean-to built against the wall of the house. The house itself was low and the lean-to was not much higher than a neighbour's coal bunker.

I took a look inside the "bridal chamber" and returned to ask Third Brother, "Why hasn't more care been taken?"

Turning his head aside on the pillow, he replied after a while, "No money. In the circumstances what we've managed to fix up isn't so bad."

"How did you hurt your leg?" I asked again.

This time he kept his mouth shut.

Younger Sister answered for him: "The planks on the roof are rotten. As he was spreading asphalt felt over the roof his weight broke one and he fell through onto the floor of the room."

As I looked at him, I felt stricken. I would not have completed my three-year studies but for his monthly ten-yuan remittance from the Great Northern Wilderness.

After supper, I said to Father, "Dad, I want to discuss something with you."

Giving me a look, Father quietly waited for me to continue. The look he gave me made me feel as if we were strangers. Was it because we had been separated for a good ten years? Or because I had become a university graduate? It was hard to say. He looked at me as an old horse might look at a deer he had brought up.

Stretching my hand out I said: "Dad, why not give Third Brother all the money you've saved up throughout these years and build a house for him?"

Looking at me strangely again, Father lowered his head. He did not speak for a long time, then said in a low voice: "I ... I have given it to him, haven't I?..."

I responded, "Dad, you've only given him two hundred and fifty yuan! Do you call that enough to build a house!"

"I ... I don't have any more ..." his voice was even lower.

"No. It's not true, Dad! You do! I know you do! You have more than three thousand yuan!" I retorted.

Father rose to his feet, his face turned a dark red. He roared at me, "You!... What nonsense you are talking! When did I ever have three thousand yuan?!"

Third Brother said from the bed, "Second Brother, why force Dad in my favour! He's been saving up money all his life and at long last he has achieved something. How could he bear to part with his savings to build me a house?" The tone revealed a son's heartfelt resentment.

I became angry and raised my voice, "Dad, that's wrong! How can Third Brother get married in that shabby coal bunker? Will your grand-son or grand-daughter be born there! You'll feel ashamed before your descendants!" Instantly, a feeling of disgust rose in my heart.

"Shut up!" Father raised a fist. But instead of falling on me, it dropped heavily to his side.

Mother, Fourth Brother and Younger Sister hurried out of the inner room and tried to drag me in.

"You!... You haven't seen me for ten years and you get at me the moment you see me again! What a son! Is this the sort of example you want to set for your younger brothers and sister? So you are a university graduate at last! Get out of here!" Father's face twitched. Fury blazed in his eyes. In his fierce and brutal voice, there were signs of the grief and misery of a bitterly disappointed man. Pointing a finger at me, he howled "get out!" again but after that was unable to utter one more word.

I struggled free from Mother and Fourth Brother's hands and announced loudly, "Dad, I'll never come back again!..." With that, I dashed out of the door.

I walked to the station without stopping and bought a ticket for a train due to leave for Beijing three hours later. Then I sat down on a bench in the waiting-hall, smoking one cigarette after another.

I did not know how much time had passed when I heard someone calling me softly. Looking up, I saw Mother and Fourth Brother standing in front of me.

Fourth Brother said to me, "Second Brother, let's go home!"

"Come on. I beg you!" added Mother.

"No." I shook my head resolutely.

Mother spoke again, "How could you quarrel with your father like that? He hasn't saved up that much money, it's true. He has given almost all his savings to your third brother and your elder brother's hospital expenses will be due early next month...."

A few curious people, male and female, gathered around, eyeing me suspiciously.

I heard an elderly woman sigh as she walked away, "All parents' tender love for children is pitiful!"

I was obviously viewed as an unfilial son.

I cut Mother short, "Mum, don't try to defend him! When I was at university, it was you yourself who wrote the letter telling me that he had saved up three thousand yuan. How can he be that stingy with his own son?"

Mother was embarrassed. Then she said, "Silly child! But it's my fault. I lied to you in the hope that you would be able to concentrate on your studies without worrying about our life at home!"

On hearing those words, I was struck dumb and looked blankly at Mother's wrinkled face. For a long time I could say nothing.

"Follow my advice. Come home and apologize to your father...." Mother pulled at my arm.

I dropped my head and wept.

I followed Mother and Fourth Brother home and apologized to Father. He did not show any sign of forgiveness.

By then Younger Sister had been at home for two years since graduating from high school, awaiting a job assignment which never came. Mother had obsequiously sought the head of our neighbourhood committee several times for help and finally she was told equivocally, "Well, next time when we are allotted quotas, I'll do what I can for you."

Mother told Father what the Head had said and suggested, "For the sake of our child, we'll have to send a gift of sorts."

Father opened a drawer and took out a paper wallet. Without looking up, he handed it over to Mother and said, "Inside is all that is left of my pension this month. I've just paid Eldest Son's hospital expenses."

There were only two ten-yuan notes in the wallet and some small change. Mother hesitated for a while before she gave one of the two notes to Younger Sister who bought something not really presentable and bore the gift to the Head's place "as a token of our appreciation ". Later she brought the gift back home untouched.

Mother asked in astonishment, "Why have you brought it back?"

Younger Sister replied dejectedly, "She won't accept it."

Mother asked again, "Because she thinks it's too small?"

"She said that we have been close neighbours for many years so it would be awkward if she accepted our gift. She said that if we insist on showing our appreciation, we can help haul back that ton of high-quality coal they bought...." Younger Sister nervously cast a sidelong glance at Father.

Father never looked up all this time. On hearing Younger Sister's words, he bowed his head even lower. After a long while, he opened his mouth: "Your Fourth Brother and I will go and do it for her...."

At that moment Fourth Brother happened to enter the room. Having been told about the situation, he said to Father with embarrassment, "Dad, the Youth League members of our factory have something on tomorrow. As branch secretary, I can't be absent."

From the inner room I heard everything. I came out and said to Younger Sister, "I'll go with Dad tomorrow."

Quite unaccountably, Father flared up: "I don't need any of you! I'll do it all by myself. I'm not yet too old to be of any use. I still have some strength left!"

......

It started to rain heavily that evening. By the next day, the rain had became even heavier. In spite of the rain, Father and I borrowed a handcart and set off. The coal was far away in a big coal yard close to a railway, some 30 *li* from our district. We made three trips with the handcart to haul back that one ton of coal. It was already dark when we finally brought back the third load. During the third trip, one of the wheels got stuck in a gap in the rails. No matter how hard Father and I tried, the wheel was stuck there as if it were welded to the rail. I first pushed together with Father, then pulled with him, and then pushed as Father was pulling and vice versa. We tried all means but to no avail. Our bodies were covered with mud and our hands with cuts and bruises. In the rain I could hear Father puffing and blowing like an ox.

Wiping off the rain on my face with one hand, I shouted to Father, "Dad, you stay here with the cart and I'll go and get help from the railway maintainance squad."

"Where has all your strength gone?" Father shoved me aside and bent over to move the cart using his shoulder with its withered muscles.

The rumbling of a train could be heard in the distance. A train was coming. A flash of lightning revealed for an instant flaccid muscles lashed ruthlessly by the heavy rain. It was the back of an old man who had lost his physical strength.

From a distance the headlight of a locomotive projected a beam in our direction.

Father was still making futile efforts to shift the cart.

I immediately started to run as hard as I could towards the squad station.

The worker on duty put out an emergency stop signal.

The train pulled up.

The worker and I ran to the handcart.

Father was still trying to move it. It was as if he simply had not noticed that a train was approaching.

"Are you damned well playing with your life?" the worker swore at him ferociously.

The beam of light from the locomotive shone directly on the cart.

Father's shoulder at last moved away from it. Slowly he raised his head. I could see clearly his desperate face, a face criss-crossed with wrinkles. Each wrinkle seemed to be an exclamation mark and there were more of them on his face than in the letter he had written to Elder Brother....

Rain was dripping down his old face.

I knew it was not just rain water. His wide-open, hollow eyes, his twitching cheeks and his trembling lips told me....

That downpour reminded me of another wet evening several years before, the evening I hid myself in between two piles of timber near our team's encampment and wept aloud....

4

One day in April, I received a telegram. It read: FATHER ARRIVES BEIJING TODAY TRAIN NO. 18. MEET AT STATION.

It was quite a few years since I had last visited home. In that time I had not seen Father. I was already 35 and was practically middle-aged. The telegram aroused in me the kind of feelings a middle-aged man has towards his aged father. They were not very strong but caused recollections of the past. The photographic plate of a man's recollections changes focus as he ages as a photo changes colour with the passage of time. Recalling the past, I felt less censorious towards Father but more to myself. After all, I had not given him much of a son's love!

The telegram was not handed to me on the day it was delivered. Somebody stuck it under my office door. That night I had stayed up late so the next morning I went to work late. Looking at my watch, I found there was still an hour and a quarter before the train was due to arrive. If I got going right away, there would be enough time to meet Father at the station. With the telegram in hand, I called a taxi. We kept starting and stopping at red lights all the way. When we finally got to the station, it was already late.

I opened the door and was about to jump out when the taxi driver caught me with one hand, "Fare!" I reached into my pocket for my wallet only to find that I had not brought it with me. I tried to explain to the driver with a flattering smile, telling him that I had come to meet someone and would pay afterwards, those and lots of other fine words. He would not let me go until I had left my I.D. card as security.

I searched in and around the station but Father was nowhere to be seen.

Despondently I returned to the taxi and pleaded with the driver to take me home and allow me to pay him for the two trips together.

The driver started the car with a snort of discontent. Seeing that we were going in the wrong direction, I smiled at his rudeness and asked, "Where are you taking me?"

"The main taxi station," the driver answered coldly. "I'm hungry. I'm going for lunch. You can get another taxi there."

I knew that I was in the wrong so I said no more.

I waited for over an hour before finally finding another taxi. The way back was smooth and fast. But I was really taken aback by the fare: twenty-three yuan!

I could not help asking, "How can it be this much?"

Glaring at me the driver said, "Including the fare from the train station to the taxi station!"

"You've charged for that section?!"

"You must be joking! You don't think you can ride a taxi for free, do you?"

When I got home, I saw Father had already arrived.

"Dad, why didn't you wait a bit longer at the station? I made a trip there for nothing!" I complained.

"I waited for a while. I didn't see you so I thought you wouldn't come to meet me there...."

"But you sent me a telegram. How could I not meet you? The idea!"

"I thought maybe you were too busy with your work to get away...."

"Dad, give me twenty-three yuan first!" I demanded.

Father was surprised at my asking for money the moment I set eyes on him and looked at me, puzzled.

I explained, "I called a taxi to meet you. The driver is waiting for the fare. I've forgotten my wallet in my office."

As if to prove my words, the taxi horn tooted several times.

Father looked as if I had told him that I had hired a spaceship to meet him. He slowly unbuttoned his coat, took out the stitches from a piece of cloth sewn into the lining, twisted out three ten-yuan bills with two fingers and handed them to me silently. From his eyes I could read the sentence in his heart: "You didn't have to make a show."

"Dad, I'll give the money back to you...." Taking the notes from him, I hurried downstairs.

When I came back again, I found Father with a very sombre countenance. He did not look at me but kept his head low, smoking away.

I realized that I had said a very stupid thing....

Father was no longer the sturdy father I had once known, nor the bright-eyed father, hale and hearty even at the age of retirement. He had become old, really old. Life had changed him into an old man. He had lost nearly all his thick black hair. What remained had turned grey. Yet his beard was superb: chequered with silvery-grey and light-yellow, it fell gracefully to about the second button of his coat. That thick beard was the only thing that bestowed on him some dignity. The hardships of life he had experienced were shown on his wrinkled face, though a trace of long-cherished unfulfilled wishes was still detectable.

Life, after all, has a firm and powerful hold on man.

At that time, my family lived in a dormitory building. We had just one room, thirteen metres square, and used the corridor as a kitchen.

On the first day of his arrival, Father sized up our "territory" in the corridor and remarked with feeling: "Second Son, you are lucky! You've been allocated a room after only a few years of employment! The corridor is so wide that it can be used for a kitchen.... You ... you've done better than me...." Father's words with their faintest hint of inferiority made me feel bad.

Father had worked all his life as a construction worker and had built countless buildings. Yet he was envious of my thirteen square metres in a dormitory building.... And he was one of those men respectfully regarded as the masters of our country....

My editorial department allowed me to use an office temporarily. Every night father and I slept in the office while my wife and child stayed at home.

Every day father helped us take our child to a nursery and fetch him, mop the floor, fetch hot water, buy food, cook meals and even do such chores as washing clothes, unpicking and washing quilts and changing gas cylinders when they are empty. He took on as much of the housework as possible.

I did not want Father, my aged father, to be reduced to my handyman. Once I told him: "Dad, don't do all these chores for us. We've become lazy since you arrived!"

Father answered gloomily, "I'm not too tired to do this bit more. I'll be content if I can stay here.... After your younger sister got married, it became really crowded at home. As a last resort, I've come to trouble you...."

Father's temperament had also changed. He became a reasonable, good-tempered, forbearing old man, in or out of the home, at all times.

Besides the household chores, Father often cleaned the public corridors, stairs, toilets and washbasins, too. Very soon, he won praise and respect from all the residents of the building. When Father first came, people would ask me, "Is that old man with a big beard your father?" Later I would be questioned thus, "Are you the son of that old man with a big beard?" As far as I was conscious of it, Father's existence was based on my personality; but in many people's eyes, I started to depend on Father's personality for existence. Now workers came to my place who had never visited us before. It had seemed possible that we should never come into contact with such people.

To my surprise, I found that Father could openly gain admission to our factory bathhouse and take a shower on days when family dependents were not allowed. He could easily get into our factory auditorium to watch a film without a ticket. He could bring home a meal on credit from our factory canteen when he forgot to bring his meal tickets. And yet everyone treated him politely and amiably. I had never enjoyed such "privileges". Using the methods available to him, Father had finally established an independent personality running parallel with mine. I no longer tried to stop him from doing public chores. I understood how necessary and how important it was to Father now that people noticed him and admitted his independent existence! That was the only thing that gave dignity to an old man, who had not had the chance to receive an education and had lost his strong physique and physical strength; his way of maintaining a psychological balance in the presence of his son, who had graduated from university and had won some reputation. I warned myself that I should treasure those achievements for Father as if they were the most valuable of objects.

The greatest change in Father was that he now showed a sincere reverence for intellectuals. In the past, he had called every kind of intellectual a "penpusher". He used to look down upon those "penpushers" who made an easy living by their pens rather than by using their physical strength. The stream of visitors I had every day now were, nine times out of ten, pure "pen-pushers". When I introduced them to Father, he would awkwardly manoeuvre his body into an unaccustomed pose: slightly bowing with his arms hanging by his side and his waist stooped. And a respectful nervous smile would appear on his face. Afterwards, he would make tea and light cigarettes for them on my behalf. While my guests and I talked with ease and fluency, he would quietly sit in a corner listening to us intently, gazing now at me and then at the guests. If we mentioned that it was time for a meal, Father would quietly get up to prepare it for us. If sometimes I totally forgot my duties as a host, he would walk in and ask me in a low voice, "The meal is ready. Do you want to have it now or in a while?" After the meal, he would as usual grab the job of washing up.

Once, after I had seen some guests off, I said to Father, "Dad, you don't need to be excessively respectful or attentive. Most of them are my colleagues or friends. It's not necessary to bother too much."

"Have I ... overacted?..." asked Father slowly, as if I was criticizing him....

Several days later, I got a letter from a friend. It read, "I went to visit you yesterday but you happened to be out. I had a chat with your father for over two hours. He really is a good father, a fine old man. I sensed that he was lonely. He told me that he had no opportunity to talk with you at all, not even for just a few minutes. Are you really that busy?..."

The letter made me feel extremely ashamed. I reproved myself sharply. It was true. I had hardly conversed with Father since his arrival, not even a casual half-hour chat between father and son. Father was no more than an old servant I had hired who did all the domestic chores for me, diligently, conscientiously, silently and unstintingly.

While I myself had been either writing endlessly or chatting with my visitors day after day....

5

At dusk one day, a girl came to my home, a stranger from another part of the country. She claimed that she had read some of my works and hoped to discuss them with me.

I took her to my office.

She was very pretty with a beautiful figure, tall and graceful. She looked dignified and elegant with a pale oval-shaped face. Her rather large eyes flashed with the light of a prolific imagination. Her pitch-black hair, neatly cut short, set off her charming face like green leaves setting off a lotus. She wore a colourful jacket with three unusual buttons which seemed to be made of bone in the shape of a crescent moon. Beneath the half-open jacket was a crimson woollen sweater. The lower part of her clothing was a pair of jeans edged with metallic gold thread at the creases and bottoms of the trouser legs and a pair of high-heeled creamy yellow shoes. She sat up straight in the sofa, her slender arms slightly outstretched and her hands clasping her knees with an habitual ease. Her bearing was gentle and refined.

My son was ill with a high temperature. When I left home, my wife was trying to pour medicine down his throat while Father was washing my clothes. I made an effort to get rid of these disturbing thoughts and to focus my attention on the conversation as best as I could. I guessed she would first of all raise some questions. But she did not. Instead, she started telling me about herself in a pleasant voice.

She had been away from home for over a month, she said, travelling to big cities all the way from the South to the North and visiting well-known young writers. Then she gave a list of their names. Some I knew in person, others I had not yet met. She continued to tell me that she adored a certain writer and his writings, could not tolerate another, appreciated so-and-so's writings but did not like the writer as a person. She was frank and open.

I enjoy talking together with frank people.

"Are you on a business trip?" I asked.

"Oh no," she shook her head and again smiled winningly. "The trip is just for fun."

"And your work unit has agreed to give you such long leave?"

"I'm under no work unit's control now —— I'm a free citizen!"

I looked at her, feeling puzzled.

Her hands unfolded from her knees. Stretching her body comfortably against the sofa, she gave a quick look around my office and observed: "Your office is big enough for five couples to dance in."

"Maybe it is. I don't know how to dance," I responded.

This time, it was she who looked puzzled. Sceptically, she gazed at me in order to see whether I meant what I said.

I smiled a shameful smile.

Her eyes moved away from me onto my writing

desk. "Bought in a free market?" she asked.

"Yes," I nodded.

"The style is very old-fashioned."

"Yes. It's rather vulgar. But very cheap."

Her eyes fixed on my face again. She looked as if I had admitted that I was a vulgar oaf.

I said, "Please go on. I'm still not quite clear about things."

"Aren't you?" doubtful expression, doubtful tone. Then she heaved a soft sigh and said flatly, "I took the entrance examinations for admission to a film institute and then a conservatory of music but failed in both. I worked in a foreign trade bureau for three months, then in a tourism bureau for half a year. Both units failed to attract me to stay longer. I drifted along in the provincial library for a year. It was the books that tied me there for that long. Later I got bored with reading so I resigned.... Perhaps I'll go to the provincial television station when I get back from this tour. It all depends on how I feel about going there...."

I understood at last. She was from another "world".

"Will your parents feel anxious if you are away from home for so long?"

"They have nothing to feel anxious about. In each city there are my father's old comrades-in-arms from the past. I can stay in their homes or in first-class hotels...."

Feeling it unnecessary to ask any more questions, I just waited for her to continue.

She was reticent for a while before speaking again. "I'm sure you can't understand me. In our childhood, my elder sister and I felt we had tasted all the delicacies of the world so we mixed up salt and sugar and sprinkled some chilli oil on top of it. Now the state of my mind is like it was when I was a little girl. I feel I'm lost. I'm fed up with everything. I've lost enthusiasm for life just as I lost my sense of taste for food in childhood—''

Still looking at her charming face, I felt sympathetic. My feeling was similar to what I might have for a tiny insect about to drown in honey.

Seeing that I was listening attentively, she went on, "I meant to get away from home in order to relieve the boredom but only find myself in a worse and worse mood. Each city is full of people —everywhere, crowds of ignorant, illiterate, muddle-headed people who are engaged in talking every day about housing problems, unemployment problems...."

I asked calmly, "Can't you put up with such people?"

"Can *you* put up with them?" She sat up straight and stared at me again. Her expression showed she was becoming disappointed at my apathy.

I did not immediately answer her.

I recalled the wet night when I had hidden myself in between two piles of timber and cried bitterly as well as the stormy night when Father and I had hauled coal for the head of the neighbourhood committee in order to help Younger Sister get a job. Drizzle or rainstorm, they were both rainy nights....

Why do the moments that stay fast in my memory all occur on rainy nights?

After all, I had dragged those rainy nights out of my life. Attached to Father, an uneducated man with narrow peasant concepts, I had got through life step by step and had grown up year by year....

"Ancient country, old nation, living in such an atmosphere, everyone will be suffocated to death!..." The pleasant voice of the girl made it difficult to divert my attention from her for long.

"Let's talk about literature!" I said.

"Literature?..." She pouted slightly, then affirmed loudly, "At present it is not possible to have literature in China! China's practical problem is its overpopulation. If two thirds of it could be cut down, the situation would be totally different!"

I replied coolly, "What a good idea! Of course the people who should be eliminated are the ones who are illiterate, muddle-headed and keep talking about housing and unemployment problems?"

The change in my mood did not arouse her attention. Knitting her brows, she commented in such a tone as to show her concerns about the country and the people, "Just today, just at the gate of your Beijing Film Studio, I saw a grey-bearded old man holding a foolish-looking child. They were there inspecting a foreign car. I felt extremely sad! I will write a psychological story to express the sort of sorrow I felt!..." She looked so lugubrious, as if she were about to cry. Or rather, as if she was trying to move me to tears. However, I was not in the least moved. I could no longer be so easily carried away by emotion as before. I was thinking that her heart must be tiny, engendering such trifling sorrows. I no longer felt any sympathy for her.

I told her that that old man with the grey beard was probably my father and that foolish-looking child in his arms my son.

"Is he ... your father?..." she flushed slightly showing some sign of embarrassment. "Please excuse me! I ... thought you were ..." she said haltingly.

"There's no point asking for excuses! Therefore I needn't give you any. I don't deny that my father is illiterate. The characters he learned in a literacy class are no more than the flowers on your colourful jacket! He is also ignorant. Because of his ignorance, because of his narrow peasant concepts, our family suffered great misfortunes! My elder sister died young because he believed in a fortune-teller rather than a doctor. My elder brother became a mental patient because he upheld only physical strength and despised education. I've forgiven him but I can't forget all those things. I loathe ignorance more intensely than you do! I understand what education means to a country or a nation better than you do! I curse all the factors that bring about this condition of illiterate backwardness!" I rose to my feet from the chair. My voice was very loud. I felt excited as if I was not just speaking to the girl in front of me but was addressing crowds of people from all walks of life.

I felt like telling her it was all right if she did not have feelings for our people. It was also all right if, élitist that she was, she showed some pity for their ignorance and illiteracy like those aristocratic ladies in the West in the novels she had read, undoubtedly adding some glamour and charm to girls like her. However, she had no right to despise them! She had no right to scorn them! It was just those people, thousands upon thousands of them, who throughout history had never had the chance to enjoy education but all that time had been making civilization, thus forming the solid foundation of our country and our nation, just as the strata of aqueous rocks had amassed and solidified through the years all over our 9,600,000 square kilometres territory! What was more, it was on their strength and sweat that the Chinese nation was relying to promote and accomplish all our causes! It was not their fault that they were ignorant or illiterate. It was the fault of history! It was the shame of each of those who lacked enthusiasm and a sense of responsibility in the vigorous development of our country and in the vitalization of our nation!

I felt like telling her that, as for herself, she was nothing but a small flower in a small patch of rich soil with adequate rain and dew. She was beautiful and delicate but had no fragrance. Her roots were thin and short so she could not reach the strata of aqueous rocks as a tree. What she scorned was exactly what she depended on for existence. She treated with indifference or even held up to mockery their most immediate worries, yet her own depression, deriving from the fact that she had nothing to worry about, and her own paltry, refined sorrow in that empty heart were, in essence, not worthy of discussion compared with all the sorrow they had experienced.

I still felt like telling her that...

I did not feel like saying anything to her.

I thought of my sick son with a high temperature. I thought I should go back to him right away.

"I'm very sorry but I can't go on talking with you!" Walking to the office door, I pushed it open —— just outside the door stood Father, dumbstruck and motionless like a block of wood, a thermos flask in one hand and an ink bottle in another.

He had come to bring hot water for us.

Obviously he had overheard something I had said so loudly a moment before.

The girl turned once to look at me as she went downstairs. She could never have imagined that I would treat her like that.

Father put down the flask and walked in silence to his bed.

We did not say anything to each other until bed time. The light was out. Lying there quietly, I could not go to sleep. Neither could Father. I knew it.

I really wanted to get out of bed and go to Father, kneel down beside him, lay my head on his chest and say to him, "Dad, forgive me for those careless words which hurt you. Please forgive me...."

Two days later, I returned home late in the evening from a friend's place. On entering, my wife told me that Father had gone.

"Gone? Where?..."

"Back to Harbin!"

"You ... why didn't you stop him?!"

"I tried but couldn't."

My son, who had just recovered from his illness, was crying, "Grandpa, I want Grandpa! I'll go and look for Grandpa!..."

"Did Father say anything before he left?" I asked.

"Nothing," answered my wife.

I shot out of the house.

At the station, I hurriedly bought a platform ticket.

The train for Harbin had just started when I dashed onto the platform. I ran after the train. I wanted to call out "Dad!..." but could not find my voice.

The train pulled out of the station.

All the people who had come to say goodbye left. I was left standing all alone on the platform. Watching the railway signal lights in the distance, I said to myself, "Dad, Dad, I love you! I will never forget I am your son, never feel ashamed to be your son! Dad, Dad, I'll make sure I'll bring you back to Beijing again!"

The signal lights in the distance had changed from red to green....

Translated by Ma Aiying

The Black Button

I went back home to Harbin last May, driven at last by a sense of nostalgia that had haunted me for a long time. I hadn't been home for seven years; for seven years, I hadn't seen my old mother.

She was alone when I arrived, as my brother, sister-in-law, sister and brother-in-law were not yet home from work. Mother was preparing supper. There was no window in the low, narrow kitchen, only one low-kilowatt lamp flickering humbly — unsteady voltage. My mother was holding a basin of rice in her trembling hands, and like a shadow in the smog, she turned dispiritedly to look at me. It was obvious that she could not see my face.

"Mama, I've come back!" I cried.

"Is that ... Shaosheng?" Mother always called me by the name I was given at birth according to clan seniority by the local official in charge of census registration. She never called me Xiaosheng, the name I had given myself in high school. It was as if she couldn't bring herself to approve of her son's new name. I did not know why and had never asked.

"Yes, Mama, it's me!" I was startled that once at home I should automatically pick up my native accent.

"Ah, ah." Mother turned around, trying to find a spot for the rice basin.

I moved into the inner room, and had scarcely put

down my suitcase than my mother entered, rice basin still in her hands. She probably could not find room for it, as the kitchen was in a terrible mess. I quickly took it from her. The room was barely larger or brighter than the kitchen. There was only one table which was cluttered with glasses, bowls and toys. I pivoted, rice basin in hand, and finally set it down for a moment on the bed.

"Why —— why didn't you write to tell me you were coming, so we could have cleaned the place up and made it a little tidier?" Mother sounded apologetic, staring at me as she sized me up. She seemed much thinner, more haggard and much older. Her face looked almost grey and waxen, and the red rims of her eyes were proof that the old eye disease was still not cured. Her clothes were dishevelled and soiled; a patch of black ash from the cooking pan remained on her coat. As I looked at her I thought of a section of a withered tree root, just dug out of the muddy ground.

I called "Mama" again, sadness rising in my heart. My throat felt as if choked by something, unable to utter a word. She had borne and reared five of us, and I, the most promising one, had become a writer. I was a consolation for her soul, a candle in her spiritual world. But far away in Beijing, I was really the least filial of sons to her. It was no exaggeration to say that I had been able to do nothing to show her my devotion since leaving for the capital. All I could do was to send home a small sum of money every two or three months.

"You've lost a lot of weight, child. I hope you aren't exhausting yourself with your writing. I don't expect you to be famous. All I want is for you to stay healthy, and safe from misfortune." Mother turned a little as she spoke, and wiped the corners of her reddenned eyelids with the front of her coat.

"I've only lost a little weight, Mama. It's certainly not a serious illness." I cheated her with a lie. I tried not to shed tears in front of her.

"Is that true?" She turned back to me, appearing again to size me up with that stare. She sighed, and then said weakly, "While you are here, you must go and see your Aunt."

"I will, in a few days," I said.

"No, you must go and see her tomorrow. I'm afraid she — she doesn't have much time left."

I was astounded.

Mother went on, "Your brothers and sisters have all been to see her. Even your brother-in-law has visited her. But you are the one she misses most. She mentions you in each letter she writes, poor woman. My life has been bitter enough, but hers has been even worse."

"Is it something serious?" It was hard to believe what Mother was saying, because my aunt was just over forty.

"Your brothers and sisters brought her to stay with us last March. They each took her to the hospital several times for examinations, but the doctors couldn't pinpoint any particular trouble. Day by day, she lost weight. She wouldn't eat or drink, and she grew frailer and thinner until she was no more than a skeleton. Poor thing.... The worst disease of all is a bitter heart. Your old teachers and classmates can wait. You must go and see your aunt first."

"Mmm."

Poor Aunt! Poor woman!

A certain misery and sadness seemed to swell in my heart. Pretending to be exhausted from travel, I lay down on the bed, feeling my eyes grow moist. Nothing in years had made me sadder than this news.

In fact, I had no aunt —— the "aunt" my mother spoke of was not my aunt by blood.

The year I was seven Mother had been working as a temporary labourer at the railway station, carrying rocks and iron, unloading coal and sifting sand — temporary labourers were always directed wherever the work was the heaviest and dirtiest, and equality between the genders was complete. Each night my mother would come home from work very late, her face black and her clothes saturated with dust.

We lived in Ping An Street then; it was before we moved to Flat Face. The house was even smaller than the present one, shabbier and darker. The floor inside was about a foot lower than the ground. To keep the rain from pouring in, a wooden plank was wedged along the threshold. You had to lift your feet high when you entered the room. Two layers of broken bricks arranged inside the threshold served as a stepping stone. First-time visitors would either knock their foreheads against the doorframe and get a painful bump, or else trip on the broken bricks and gasp in panic.

Although our little house did boast a window, half of it was sunk below the ground. The house's settling over time had warped the windowframe until it was so misshapen that it could not be opened. No squarecut glass could thus replace the broken windowpanes, so we'd had to cover the window with sheets of heavy paper. The house was privately owned, and the landlord would not reduce the rent however ramshackle condition of the structure.

We had two rooms. The outer room we used as a kitchen in the summertime, and in the winter, we moved the stove into the inner room for heat. There, my mother and we five children squeezed together to sleep on the *kang*. We stored everything in the outer room: cabbages, turnips and potatoes; the water vat, grain box, firewood, coal bucket — scarcely an inch was unoccupied.

I remember one winter day when it had been snowing heavily from morning till night. Mother was very late returning from work, and she'd brought a stranger home with her. "Lower your head ... lift your feet ... step slowly, now, and carefully," we heard her say. She entered the room first, her face as black as usual, and then reached back to take the stranger's hand. Thanks to Mother's careful guidance, the fellow didn't bruise his head or frighten himself stepping on the loose bricks. She led him into the room. His face was even blacker than Mother's was, so it was impossible to guess his age. But from that filthy face it was easy to see he was a temporary labourer like she was, and had no doubt spent the day unloading coal. Like my mother, the stranger wore a dog fur hat, a knee-length cotton quilted vest, and rubber-soled cotton shoes.

Mother grabbed a brush from off the *kang* and started brushing snow from the stranger's clothes, talking all the while. "Look how shabby this house is! These are my children.... Shaosheng, quick, fetch us some water to wash!''

A pair of eyes were all that were clean on the fellow's coal-blackened face, but the eyes looked a little unhappy and embarrassed. He remained motionless by the door. It seemed he found our house in even worse condition than he had expected, and he didn't quite know how to react.

I filled up half a basin of cool water and gently placed it at his feet. Seeing that there was not enough room to wash his face, the stranger picked the basin up and, without a word, took it into the outer room. Mother, pulling off her hat and vest, followed him in order to clean her own sooty face.

Twice she returned for more water.

We children stood together in the inner room, eyeing one another with expressions of surprise and wonderment.

At last, Mother brought her guest back in, and our wonder multiplied by ten —— the fellow was female: a teenage girl.

We lived in an area occupied by a metal wire factory that was expanding, and a new three-storey building had just gone up. All of our neighbours had moved away. Only our ramshackle house remained as the property owner, our landlord, was haggling with the factory administrators over a higher price for the land. We lived in the shadow of the tall new factory building, in the midst of construction debris that had not been removed.

No one had come to see us for quite some time after the neighbours had moved out. Without visitors the house was extremely lonely for the children. And with no relatives in Harbin, our loneliness was all the more unbearable. In our naive hearts, we all yearned for someone to know — in this city behind this tall factory, surrounded by rubbish, a little family was living. As long as that someone would meet us face to face, we would offer our most heartfelt gratitude and affection. The young girl that snowy evening appeared before us as if by magic, and her appearance filled us with wonder and delight.

She was very pretty; at least we thought she was. She had left her heavy soiled vest in the outer room, and taken off her overalls, and she wore a short cotton quilted coat with black flowers on a scarlet background. It looked quite new. She was half a head taller than Mother, an admirable height for a woman. Though she was dressed in cotton-padded clothing, we could see that she was slender, not too fat and not too thin. Her face was pink and glowing, probably because she had just scrubbed it with cold water. But the coal dust was not completely gone from around her eyes, and they looked as if they were painted, large and full of spirit.

To my brothers and sisters and me, she seemed completely adult, but this grown-up couldn't have been more than seventeen or eighteen years old. We all lay in a row on our stomachs on the *kang*, staring at her foolishly.

She turned slightly away from our staring, embarrassed, pulling her thick pigtail in front of her chest with both hands. Then she said to Mother in a delicate voice, "My sister, have you got a comb?"

"Yes, yes," Mother answered, pulling out a drawer under the cracked table. She handed her the only comb we had, which had lost not a few of its teeth.

The girl unbraided her pigtail and began to comb her hair.

"Get away from here!" Mother scolded us. "We've got only one *kang*, and you're sprawled across every inch of it!"

We scooted over to huddle in one corner of the *kang*.

"Sit down, sit down," Mother said, nudging the girl gently to the edge of the *kang*.

I asked in a low voice, "Mama, should I heat up some food for you? We've eaten already."

"I'll do it myself," said Mother. "Just clean a couple of cabbages and wash a turnip, and I'll make some soup." Throwing a glance at our guest, she went and sat down next to her. She gave the girl's shoulder an easy push, "Why don't you say something?"

The girl kept combing her hair, stroke by stroke, without so much as looking up. Mother spoke again.

"If you don't like this house of mine, you can stay with me just for tonight, and then tomorrow I'll see what I can do to help you. Maybe we can find a better place for you to live. But if you think you can make do with our home, you can stay here for good. I won't kick you out, no matter how long you stay. And if I have something to eat, you will have something to eat; if I have something to cover myself with, you will, too."

The girl still refused to look up or to utter a single word. That wooden comb kept moving, slowly, slowly, over her long black hair, until the hair was smooth as satin. We children were very disappointed by the visitor's silence, thinking that she didn't care to stay with us for long. I stole a glance at her as I picked the brown leaves from a cabbage and washed a turnip. How I longed to hear her say "Yes, I will stay," or see her nod her head. But she seemed to have gone mute, and dropped her head still lower.

Mother appeared somewhat abashed when the girl refused to answer. She rose slowly to her feet and went to chop the cabbage.

"How much would you charge per month, Sister?" Suddenly she raised her head, and spoke in a nearly imperceptible voice.

"Listen to you! Charge! What are you talking about?" Mother stopped cutting cabbage and wheeled around. "This house isn't mine. And I'm no profiteer — If you want to stay here, I won't charge you a single cent."

The girl's face which struck me as beautiful now broke into a smile like a flower blooming. "Then I will stay with you for good," she murmured happily with her head dropped again, and went on combing her hair.

"But we must think of some proper way for the children to address you," Mother smiled. "Since you have called me sister, and since you're the same age as my own younger sister who died, from now on you shall be the children's aunt. Is that all right?"

In a voice which sounded like a child promising to be obedient, the girl just murmured "Mm-hmm," and, putting down the comb, began to braid her hair.

"Did you all hear?" our mother turned and said. "From this day on, you call her 'aunt'."

"Aunt!" yelled all the brothers and sisters as if with one voice, and tumbled toward her like kittens.

She turned half way towards us, with the smile I already loved. I felt as if our shabby room was suddenly filled with a radiant light.

In the midst of all the hollering, the heart of this seven-year-old boy was filled with a strange excitement —— She'd be my aunt from then on! And such an aunt! My little wooden pistol painted black, my box of picture books, those dozen colourful marbles, that small sparrow living in the drawer —— all of my treasure put together couldn't equal this. To me, she was a godsend, already as dear as if she really were a member of my family.

In the past Mother had never taken the trouble to cook for herself if we children had finished eating by the time she got home from work. Her supper would be only a few bites of whatever we kept for her. That day, though, she was very late and we could see that she was very tired, still she pulled herself together to cut the cabbage into thin slices and stir it up to make a dish. She sliced the turnip, too, and made half a pan of soup. Turning the flour bag inside out she shook out enough to make a few fried cakes with a lot of oil   we had never seen her use quite so much oil to cook one meal.

Like Mother, Aunt was not one to do anything grudgingly. Otherwise, how could the two of them have polished off such a big dish of cabbage and drunk up all that soup? After they'd had their supper, I hurried to clear the table and wash the dishes. The way I felt that night, I was more than willing to do chores I usually avoided. When Aunt offered to do the dishes herself, Mother held up her hand, saying, "There will be plenty of time for you to help later. Today, you must not trouble yourself." Aunt smiled back at her. I thought that I could never have enough of her smiling — she could make your whole being light with that smile.

"Tonight you can squeeze in beside me on the *kang*," Mother told her. "Tomorrow, we'll clean up the outer room and make a bed for you." Our new aunt bobbed her head slightly. In the eyes of the children, she was a grown-up girl, but to Mother, she really seemed to be a young sister, a child. Her manner to Mother was obedient and mild.

When Mother started preparing the *kang*, all the brothers and sisters voluntarily huddled together to make a space for Aunt. All of our quilts were worn out and the white quiltcases were dirty. Mother was a diligent housekeeper, and she would undo the quilts and wash them nearly once a month. But even that wouldn't keep the quilts clean enough. The *kang* itself was dirty, because the three dirty walls peeled a great deal everyday. Besides that, our little bodies were pretty dirty, too. In the summer, it wasn't hard to keep ourselves clean — Mother would put a big bucket of water outside the room and strip us down to bathe us in it. But throughout the winter, bathing was out of the question.

My brothers and sisters were very young after all, and so immersed in the joy of gaining a beautiful aunt that they never thought of being ashamed of dirty quilts. But I was already seven years old, and I felt a hot blush spread across my face. It was the first time a sense of shame had left a mark on my pride, and not a shallow one, though not too lastingly deep.

I added more warm water to the basin and put it at

her feet, saying politely, "Aunt, please wash your feet."

"Ah!" she said, as if surprised, looking first at me and then at Mother.

"Go ahead," Mother told her, "Wash your feet."

"How can I behave like a princess?" the girl replied. "Sitting here waiting for the children to bring me water to wash my feet in. Sister, you must have a talk with the children. Never let them behave this way to me in the future." It was almost as if she were begging.

"Don't worry," Mother gently reassured her. "They're only showing you the love they feel, from the bottom of their hearts. They're so happy they've got you —— can't you see that?"

"I'm not stupid," she said. "How can I fail to see that?" Looking me up and down she went on, "Do you go to school?"

"Yes," I answered.

"What grade are you in?"

"Just started first grade."

"Then your aunt will help you with your studies later on. Your aunt is a primary school graduate!" There was a fragment of pride in the lovely smile.

I couldn't help smiling back, saying "Good!"

"Our Shaosheng studies very hard," Mother put in, "and he wears two dashes*. He gets a certificate of merit every year."

---

*Two dashes is one of the three signs indicating a leader in the Young Pioneer, an organization for superior students at primary schools. (Translator's note)

"Well, you should work hard," said Aunt. "With your father working far away from home, and your mother working so hard to support you and bring you up, you must work extra hard at your studies and not let her down."

I nodded in silence.

Aunt turned to Mother, "It's no easy task for you."

Mother sighed deeply. "No easy task indeed. Sometimes I get tired of life."

I moved back quietly to the corner of the *kang* and pulled my textbook from my satchel, took off my shoes, and lay down facing the wall, holding the book to read.

Mother continued to urge Aunt, "Wash your feet —— you must be tired, we've been unloading coal all day."

Aunt refused to be first to use the water anyway. Eventually, Mother washed first, then Aunt followed. But then she just sat still at the edge of the *kang*, dangling her bare feet, stalling before taking off her clothes.

When Mother encouraged her, she said, "I'll wait —— my nephew is reading."

"No, I'm not any more," I said, shoving the book beneath the pillow.

Until this night, we children had always drifted into dreams the moment we turned in. This time, somehow, we didn't feel the least bit like sleeping. Like my brothers and sisters, I was stretched out on my stomach in the quilt, staring at aunt. I drank in the sight of her as if I could never get enough. Mother kept urging her to get ready for bed.

She lowered her head, and whispered, "I will wait until the children are asleep. I feel ashamed in front of all these nephews."

Mother patted each of our heads and ordered "Close your eyes, close your eyes, all of you —— close your eyes and get to sleep!" As soon as one of us did as she said, another's eyes would pop open again. The complete novelty of the situation had us so worked up that we couldn't begin to feel sleepy as if Aunt would be gone when we woke up.

"These children, they're really naughty!" Mother, pretending to be angry, threw a look at Aunt and couldn't help chuckling as she turned off the light. The room was instantly pitch dark, so black you couldn't see your hand in front of your face.

In the darkness we could hear the rustling of Aunt taking off her clothes. There was silence for a moment, then we heard her whisper to Mother, "Those men who work with us are really terrible. They won't stop pestering me and making lewd remarks."

"Just take no notice of it. The more you take it to heart, the more they like it. Not one of them is any good." Mother whispered back.

"I don't dare get angry. I'm afraid they'll really start to bully me if I offend them."

"Don't be afraid of them! If one man dares to push you around, he won't have heard the last of it from me. Your big sister is a peaceable woman, but one thing I won't stand for is bullying. You're my sister, and anyone who harasses you, harasses me."

So that's the way Aunt became a part of our household. Perhaps she was all the dearer to us being kin by choice, and not by blood.

Later on, I was told by Mother that she wasn't just a graduate of primary school, she was also a member of the Communist Youth League. She was from a village in Double-Town County, about one hundred *li* from Harbin. Life in her family had been hard, and she'd come to Harbin alone when she heard that young labourers were being recruited in the city. Before she came to our house, she had spent her nights sleeping in the railway station.

Her presence brought about a number of changes in our home. For one thing, we soon stopped relieving ourselves here and there outside the house. Aunt helped us to build a simple toilet nearby. Because she valued cleanliness, the rest of us came to take pleasure in such things.

We took two broken boxes out of the inner room and arranged them in the outer room as a bedframe. One night, Mother and I went out and got a couple of scaffolding planks from the construction site, and with them we fashioned a makeshift bed in the outer room for Aunt. The cabbages and turnips we stored under the bed. A thick frost had formed on every wall of the outer room from the drafts that swept through. My brothers and sisters and I scraped off the frost with a spatula and filled in all the holes and cracks with old cotton balls. Still, we worried that Aunt might get cold at night, and so we moved the stove into the outer room, dug a hole in the partition wall, and added two sections of the pipes as a heat duct to the inner room. That way the inner room was just as warm and appeared more spacious as well.

Before Aunt came to us, Mother had never been

able to even think of doing such things, much less to find the inclination. I, as a small boy, could not have thought of them either. But now that Aunt was one of us, I thought of doing any number of things without needing any reminding from Mother. And so there soon were small improvements in our home, as there were in ourselves.

About a month before Spring Festival, Mother suddenly seemed preoccupied with something. One day she whispered to me behind Aunt's back that she was worried Father might be annoyed when he came home for Spring Festival and found a strange woman there. Knowing what was on her mind, I grew privately concerned as well. Father would never accept an aunt. If he were not outraged, it would be a miracle.

Mother asked me to write Father a letter, telling him that things were fine at home, and listing a number of reasons why it would be better to postpone his visit until summer.

Naturally, Aunt knew nothing of this. Almost everyday she asked Mother, "When will my brother-in-law be coming home?" Mother would answer, "We're not sure yet if he'll return for Spring Festival or not."

"Well, write him, Sister; be quick! He hasn't been home for two years, has he? Don't you miss him?"

Mother answered lightly, "No."

Aunt smiled and said, "I think you're cheating me. Even if you don't miss him, don't you think the children do?"

"Oh, the children have probably forgotten him by now."

Hearing this, my brothers and sisters raised an immediate protest. "No! No! We've been waiting for ages to see Father again!"

Mother couldn't bring herself to say any more.

Father did write saying that he wouldn't be coming home that year. My brothers and sisters set up a terrible howl when I read them the letter. Mother and I just exchanged looks in silence. I felt pretty much as she did: relieved and guilty at the same time.

Aunt began to reproach Father for his negligence. "What a man! With such a big family he hasn't seen for two whole years, he simply chooses not to visit! Sister, let me write and ask him if he's thinking of his family at all."

Mother put on a fierce face and said, "No, no letters to that man. He's not thinking about the family, so we won't think about him either."

Aunt's own father, an honest and kind-hearted peasant, arrived in Harbin from the village to take his daughter home for Spring Festival. But she didn't want to go. She told her father, "This is the first Spring Festival since I've known my new sister. My brother-in-law's not coming home this year, and she and the children will be awfully lonely if I go away. I have to spend this Festival with them."

Her father stayed with us for just two days. He didn't want to compel his daughter to leave with him, and so he went, alone and disappointed. He told my mother he was leaving Aunt in her care.

And so, though Father didn't visit us, we had a very happy festival, thanks to Aunt.

We sent off the Kitchen God. We said prayers to our ancestors. We lit firecrackers. We ate New Year's dumplings. Aunt helped Mother cook a few delicious dishes, and we bought a bottle of cheap grape wine.

While we were eating the New Year's dumplings, Mother set an additional place at the table. "Mama," I protested, "There's an extra dish and set of chopsticks."

"No, they're not extra. Those are for your Papa. Your Papa has not spent a Spring Festival with us for so long —— we'll just pretend he's with us tonight, and that the family is all together."

Aunt shot her a glance and filled two cups with wine. Handing one to Mother and holding the other in both hands, she said very solemnly, "Sister, will you drink this cup to my brother-in-law? Brother-in-law, to you!" So saying, she lifted the cup and drank all the wine. Her face blushed like peach blossom. Mother also drank all her wine in one go.

After the Spring Festival, the weather got milder. Soon it was April, and we found life becoming more difficult. In addition to Aunt, we also had another huge family living with us: the innumerable bedbugs.

They thrived on our blood to produce their offspring. They were at us all night, and we tossed and turned in misery on the *kang*. Row upon row of raised red bites covered our bodies. My youngest sister was so badly bitten that she cried and cried, and couldn't even fall asleep at night. I sought pleasure of a sort in the hardship, and worked out a riddle for Aunt:

> *When the sun has gone down and the Tang*
>   *monk's asleep,*
> *Up the slope of the mountain the Red Monster*
>   *creeps.*

*To assure his long live the monk's flesh he would
take —
But The Pig will awaken and swing his great rake.**

It seemed that she'd got it, but she didn't say what
the answer was. She just kept dipping cotton balls in
salty water and swabbing the bites on our bodies.
Eventually she sighed and told Mother, "We've just
got to do something about this. The children are half
bitten to death."

Mother looked at us with sympathy. "We've tried
everything, but we just can't seem to wipe them out."

The next day, Aunt didn't go to work. After Mother
left, she said to me, "Come along. We have some
business to attend to."

I followed her without asking what was going on.
She led me to the bank and withdrew some money.
The teller seemed puzzled.

"You just deposited this money yesterday. Taking it
out already?"

"For an emergency," Aunt replied.

"Twenty yuan? You want to withdraw it all?"

"Yes."

Aunt led me to a place where we rented a handcart,
and then, pushing the cart, I followed her to the market and we bought two straw mattresses. After we returned home, she went out to the worksite and asked
for a bucket of calcium carbide.

Under Aunt's direction, we all carried out the old
broken furniture from the room, and mixed the chemi-
cal in water with some pesticide. I wanted to help her,
but she wouldn't let me, lest I should burn my hands.

---

*Refers to a classical tale, *Journey to the West*. (Translator's note)

She fashioned a brush with old strips of cloth, and used it to wash all the walls. Then she boiled several kettles of water and poured it into all the cracks in the old furniture.

Before Mother got back from work, we had cleaned up the room and placed the new straw mattresses on the *kang*. The walls had several ugly yellow spots after the washing, for there was moisture in them. But Aunt was full of ideas: she went to the store and bought several pictures, which she put up over the blotches. When Mother walked in the door, she was so amazed she couldn't speak for several moments.

Aunt's hands were burned and blistered from the concoction. But when she looked at Mother, the corners of her mouth curled into a beaming smile. Mother tried to pay her back for the straw mattresses, but Aunt wouldn't hear of it.

"It wasn't easy for you to save that little bit of money," Mother said. "And you've got your old parents at home. You must take the repayment."

"Sister, if you force the money on me, I'll move out," was Aunt's angry reply.

Mother had to leave it at that.

She took Aunt's poor burned hands into her own, and tears ran down her face.

That night, we slept soundly.

Not long after, the landlord brought a suit against Mother with the neighbourhood committee. He claimed Mother was so greedy that she'd brought a tenant into her rented home and become a profiteer. The neighbourhood cadres listened, and came to the house to question Mother. Although she explained everything, they refused to take her word.

"Where could you find so kind-hearted a person? Offering free accommodation to someone who's neither relative nor friend...." They openly displayed their suspicion.

Mother was livid. She snapped right back at them, "If you don't believe me, do as you please!"

Again, while Aunt was at home, they came for a second investigation.

Aunt was no less blunt in her response. "So you think that since my sister took me in, she has to be a profiteer. Only someone with a greedy mind could spin such a story."

The committee cadres still would not take the women's word, groundlessly assuming that the two had worked hand in glove to rehearse answers ahead of time. So they goaded on the landlord to take his suit against Mother all the way to court.

Mother soon received a summons. It was the first time she's been compelled to have any dealings with the law. Aunt, being a country girl with even less experience, grew quite uneasy. "Better just let me move out," she said.

"Have you anywhere to go?" Mother asked her.

"I can sleep at the station again," Aunt suggested.

We were distraught when we heard that. "You can't do that! You can't move out, not for any reason! Mama, don't let her leave!"

"Do you hear what they're saying?" Mother asked her. "They won't allow you to go. Besides, if you moved out, those groundless accusations would seem true. 'If you have the truth, you can travel all over the world,' I'm not afraid of the court. If you want to go sleep at the station, don't call me Sister any more.''

Mother came back from the court with the triumphant air of a proud victor. Aunt demanded, ''Sister, did you win?''

''I had the truth, eh?'' said Mother. ''How could I lose?''

''Thank God!'' breathed Aunt. ''Since you left, my heart's been in my throat.''

''Haven't seen much of the world,'' said Mother.

''Sister, what did the court ask you, how did you answer?''

''Why bother yourself about it? It's all nonsense. The court told the landlord, in my presence, that first, his suit was groundless; second, he must not make any more trouble for us. He can't order us to move out unless we choose to. Furthermore, he was criticized for accepting rent without maintaining the property!''

Aunt gazed at her in admiration. ''Good for you, Sister!''

''What's good for me?'' snorted Mother. ''I went to the court with pent-up anger. If he hadn't taken this all the way to court, I could have lived with it.''

Now it was Aunt who wanted to stir things up. ''Let me go with you to the landlord! Let me avenge you and give him a taste of his own medicine.''

''With truth on our side, there's no need to press the issue. Forget it. Let's give him two yuan extra for the rent so he won't make trouble for us later, concocting something out of nothing.''

Hearing that, Aunt looked at Mother and said nothing for quite a while.

After May Day, the weather grew still warmer. The rubbish heaps surrounding the house had been encased in layers of dirty ice from the slop water we'd tossed out during the winter. During the days, as the sun beamed down, the ice melted and streamed down the rubbish heaps, making a stinking muddy mess out of the road.

One day, Aunt said to Mother, holding her hands behind her back, "Can you guess what my family has sent to me?"

"Shoes?" Mother tried.

Aunt shook her head. Mother thought for a minute and asked, "Clothes?"

"You'll never guess if you keep thinking of something to wear."

Mother smiled. "Is it something to eat?"

"You might say it's something to eat, but you can't eat it right away." Aunt brought her hands toward Mother. "Vegetable seeds, and flower seeds as well."

She emptied a small cloth bag, and the packets dropped onto the *kang*. "Look," she said, "These are cabbage seeds. These are spinach, and these are rape ... Ah! And also cucumber seeds and pea seeds. Sister! Look at all these flower seeds! Marigolds, roses, garden balsams, more than ten different kinds."

"How come your family happened to think of sending seeds to you? Where do we plant them?"

"I wrote and asked for them. I want to clear away the rubbish and make a garden with my nephews."

"Fancy you thinking of such things. Ah, you have the heart of a girl after all."

"As we live," said Aunt, "we should try to live joyfully."

The next day was Sunday. Under Aunt's direction,

we began to flatten the rubbish heaps and sow the vegetable and flower seeds in small plots, which we divided with ridges. Before long, the old rubbish heaps had turned into meadows of green. In July and August, the peas and cucumbers were climbing up the stakes and flowers were in full bloom. The four sides of our shabby little house had become a true garden spot, a riot of colour; red and green, purple and yellow — very pleasant to look at.

It was simply beautiful. The garden drew all sorts of dragonflies and butterflies. It also attracted the women who worked in the wire factory. They came in threes and fours during breaks and after work, to look at the flowers and to ask for some to take with them. Aunt was generous, and satisfied every request. She made a fine impression on them.

How could two women and a bunch of kids live such a full and rewarding life in that shabby earth dwelling hidden behind the huge factory — a place that seemed cut off from the rest of the city? The women workers often expressed their wonder when they beheld our garden.

In the evenings, my brothers and sisters and I would not be confined in the house. We sat on a plank listening to conversation of these two women, whom we felt were the dearest in the world, and taking in our meadow, our flowers, the beauty of our big garden. We had rarely enjoyed anything good and beautiful in life. The loveliness that surrounded us now had all been brought by our Aunt, a country girl.

Amid the refreshing fragrances and vibrant colours some comprehension was awakened in our tender souls. We carried on an innocent but serious contemplation, pondering what the beauty of life really meant, and wondering what gratitude was, why gratitude was necessary. In those moments, I understood that our Aunt was the most beautiful woman I had ever known.

The topic that most often occupied the women was the change from temporary labourer to a worker on permanent basis. Was there any other topic but the change that could fascinate them? Hardly a moment went by when Aunt and Mother were not dreaming of that. The longing often made Aunt's face light up for joy, and could ignite a gleam of hope in Mother's eyes such as we had rarely seen. I knew the idea of the change was their common happiness.

One evening I sat before Aunt with my elbows on her knees, playing with her long pigtail, unbraiding it and braiding it again, having a wonderful time. Mother looked at me and then at Aunt, and said with a sigh, "I've never picked up anything by chance before in my life. How lucky that I've found something dearer than gold."

Naive as a child, Aunt asked, "What have you picked up? Tell me about it!"

"I've found a sister for myself and an aunt for my children."

Aunt contemplated Mother for quite a while, then nestled up to her. "I'll make certain that you've really found me. I will never be lost again."

Mother spoke in a voice equally quiet. "Though you say so now, do you really think that you can stay with me for life? Never marry, never have a family?" She turned and scolded me. "Look at you, such a big boy, behaving like a child. You don't understand anything. Get away from here and play somewhere, stop sticking to your Aunt like that.''

Aunt was smiling all the while. I blushed, embarrassed. She put her arm around my neck, preventing me from retreating, and said, "Shaosheng, when you grow up and go to university and become a cadre or something, you won't refuse to recognize your aunt?''

I answered her loudly, swearing, "If I refuse to recognize you, may lightning strike me dead in my tracks!''

Aunt chuckled, and Mother couldn't keep from smiling, too. Aunt's arm felt so soft and smooth against my neck. I said to myself, "My aunt, I've got as much love for you as I have for my mother.'' I couldn't resist burying my face against her arm.

One day, Aunt and Mother looked gloomy when they returned from work. Aunt's work status had been changed from temporary to permanent, but Mother had been laid off because of labour cutbacks. She could not return to work the next day. Mother was obviously very sad and disappointed, and her pride was badly hurt. I was also sad and worried. Poverty had made me understand things at a very early age. I knew what it would mean to our family that Mother had lost her job.

"You are too docile! Did ever a day pass when you worked less hard than the others? So many sly and deceitful people have been promoted. Why was it that nobody but you got laid off, with just one word from the boss? That's bullying! I'm going to reason it out with them for you. If there's no justice for you, I'm going to quit.''

"I won't let you go and intervene for me." It was the first time I'd heard Mother speak to Aunt in such a way. Aunt was at a loss, and she looked at Mother astonished. Mother softened her tone. "My foolish sister. You came all the way from the country, and went through such ordeals to get a job. Now, you've been promoted. How proud your parents would be of you! You certainly must not intervene for me in this matter — it could get you sacked. You've been promoted — I'm happy for you — " Mother couldn't go on.

Aunt threw herself into her arms, sobbing "Sister!"

Not long after the promotion, Aunt moved out to live in the collective dorm of the factory. Our Aunt was gone. We all found it hard to let her go, but we said nothing to stop her, realizing, after all, that she was going to a better life.

She found it difficult to leave us, as well. The day she moved out, she cried like a child.

But though Aunt had left our home, she didn't forget us. Hardly a Sunday went by when she didn't come to visit us. She was still dearer to us than a blood relative.

Father had promised in his letter that he would visit us during the summer, but he didn't actually get back until just two days before National Day. Once he arrived, he naturally heard a lot about "Aunt this" and "Aunt that". No wonder he'd question Mother: "Where did you find this 'sister' of yours? How did she get to be the children's aunt?"

"It doesn't cost anything," Mother retorted. "Why stick your nose into it?"

"You bet I'll stick my nose into it," he answered

gravely. "I'm not about to let some woman who's got nothing to do with our family come into this house and influence my children."

Mother's answer was equally solemn. "Not even if the influence is for the best?"

"If I can't see her in a favourable light," said Father, "I won't allow her in this house."

"So if she comes, you'll kick her out?"

"I most certainly will," was Father's edict.

"Well, you can ask the children if they'll let you do that," said Mother.

"Do you mean to say any one of them would dare to get in my way?"

Mother gave a loud "Harrumph!" and stopped arguing. Later, in private, she said to me, "Go and see your Aunt tonight. Tell her not to visit us this month. Wait until Father's gone back to the Northwest." After supper, I slipped away without his seeing me.

"Why won't you let me see your father? Is he so fearsome? Has he got three heads and six arms?" Hearing what I had to say, Aunt was bewildered. I spoke quite frankly.

"Mama's afraid that Father won't like you. If you come, he may kick you out."

"So it's like that." Aunt thought for a moment and said, "Go back and tell your mama that I won't visit you, that's all." She wanted me to stay with her for a while, but I was scared that if I got home too late my father would question me. So I hurried off.

The next morning, who should turn up but Aunt. She appeared dressed in a green skirt and a lovely flowered blouse, her face wreathed in smiles. Mother had one foot in and one foot out of the door, and when she confronted Aunt she exclaimed, "Oh! How did you happen to come by?"

"I've come to see my brother-in-law, since he's travelled thousands of *li* to come home." She stepped into the room as she spoke. Mother followed her quickly inside.

When my brothers and sisters saw who it was, they swarmed around her, crying "Aunt, Aunt!" Father, shaving before the broken mirror, caught sight of her face in it. He went on shaving without speaking or turning around.

"Father," said Mother, "the children's Aunt is here."

Father had to respond. He grunted "Hmph." But still he refused to look in Aunt's direction.

Mother compensated for his coldness with her warmth. She nudged Aunt to sit on the *kang* and took the small package from her hands. Reproachfully she said, "You bought something for the children again? How much money are you making? Buying things all the time___"

Aunt smiled, "It's not for the kids this time. I've bought something for my brother-in-law."

Father finished shaving. He put away his razor and took the basin into the outer room to wash his face, without a word to Aunt. Mother hurried after him. We all looked at Aunt uneasily. She tried to jolly us with pleasantries. After a while, I saw Mother give Father a push, and he was propelled into the inner room.

He lowered himself reluctantly to the *kang*. "So," he said, "have you got the day off today?"

"Mmmm." Aunt stopped playing with the

children. "Brother-in-law, I can see that you're by no means an ill-tempered man."

"Whoever said I was?"

"No one but my sister. She was afraid you'd kick me out if I came over."

Father answered, "Nothing of the kind."

"I didn't think my brother-in-law would treat me like that." Then she asked, "How many days was the train trip from the Northwest to the Northeast?"

"Three days and three nights."

"Are the sand storms very strong there?"

"Very. They can push a man from a walk to a run."

"And does it snow there in winter?"

"Yes."

"I hear the Northwest has a water shortage."

"Nowhere else is there less water. Cows trail the water truck wherever it goes, to lick the tank. They'll follow a truck a dozen *li* or so. The cows are so thirsty, their eyes begin to water at the sight of something to drink. Some die on their feet from dehydration. And because there's no moisture in their bodies, you can hardly skin them." Father was like a radio switched on at the mention of the Northwest. It was impossible to turn him off. He talked on and on, and Aunt listened, rapt and wide-eyed, as if she were listening to fantastic tales.

Father didn't kick her out that day. That day, Aunt had lunch and then supper with us. She didn't leave until it was dark. After she was gone, Father said to Mother, "This Aunt is not such a bad person. Quite an honest country girl."

"Honest or dishonest," said Mother with some annoyance in her voice, "It's not your business to flatter her." Father lowered his head, chuckling.

Before he left for the Northwest, Father offered Aunt his old watch.

Aunt had been in town over a year now, and she'd lost her country tan. Her eyes were brighter, even more given to smiling. Her disposition was sweeter, more gentle; her figure more graceful and slender. All in all she had grown more beautiful.

The young fellows from the wire factory often stopped me and grinned cheekily, "Ai, little lad! Who's that big pigtail that keeps coming to your home? What's she to you?"

Not without pride, I answered, "She's my aunt."

"Go ask her if she'll let me be your uncle!"

I wasn't sure if that was good talk or bad talk, so I swore at them. Instead of getting mad, they broke out laughing. To me, not one of the hundreds of young women workers at the factory was as good looking as Aunt. I thought I had plenty of reasons to be proud.

I remember one Sunday, the summer of the next year, Aunt came to see us, wearing a brand new poplin blouse, khaki pants and a new pair of leather shoes. She never overdressed, and still looked simple even in flowered prints.

Mother didn't speak for quite a while. She seemed lost in thought. Aunt was a bit embarrassed under her gaze, and dropped her head. "Why are you looking at me like that?"

"I think you're becoming more and more beautiful."

Aunt raised her head slowly. "In the past, when people said I was good-looking, I never believed it. These days, even I feel I'm a little prettier."

"Flattering yourself! Isn't that shameful!" Mother said.

"Isn't it true? City people wash their faces with warm water and fragrant soap. Isn't that enough to make them fairer?"

"That's true," smiled Mother, and she added, "When you went home again last, didn't you go to get engaged to someone?"

Aunt flushed, and said loudly, "No, no __ "

"Yes or no, it's no business of mine," said Mother.

"Why not? You're my older sister, I'm your younger sister."

"Let me ask you, then. Where are you going to find your husband? In the country, or in the city?"

Realizing that Mother was serious, she thought for a while, and asked, "What do you think?"

"You should certainly find one in the city. Now you have become a city girl. Didn't you register as a resident at the factory?"

Aunt nodded. Mother continued, "All the more reasons to find one in the city."

Mother spoke again. "I only hope that if you've got your eye on someone, you'll bring him here and let me have a look at him, so I can tell you what I think. After all, I've eaten more salt than you over the years. I'll be able to tell at a glance whether he's a man of character."

Aunt looked down again and didn't speak for quite a while. Mother asked, "Don't you believe me, after all this time?"

Aunt remained silent. Then she asked, "Would you tell me please, how you can tell — when a man seems good to a woman, whether or not he is sincere?"

Mother thought for a moment, and said, "Eight to ten, you've got your eye on some man."

Aunt looked at her quickly. "No, no— "

Mother said, "Whether or not a man is sincere with a woman, nobody else can tell. Only the woman can feel that in her heart." Aunt dropped her head again without speaking. She looked lost.

In the autumn, there were continuous rainstorms. The waters of the Songhua River rose several metres above the level of the streets of Harbin. That year we had the worst flood since 1936.

Since flood prevention efforts were undertaken in time, the waters didn't overwhelm the city. Men and women, all the adults in Harbin, were mobilized day and night in the desperate effort to fight the flooding at the various dams.

We didn't see Aunt for many days. Mother conjectured that she must be out there fighting the flood. Many people spent the night of the Moon Festival out on the dams.

In the end the flood was curbed and Mother said that surely Aunt would come in a few days.

We awaited her anxiously. For over a month, she didn't show up. No one could have imagined how I missed her.

Although the flood had been defeated, the autumn rains kept on. The storm was raging violently one midnight, the thunder crashing, flashes or lightning illuminating our shabby room through the latticed window. We had gone to bed, but I hadn't fallen asleep. Suddenly I thought I heard a faint knocking at the door.

"Mama," I said. "There's someone at the door."

"Who would come out at this time?" she replied.

But I was certain. "It is a knock, Mama. You listen."

Mother strained her ear for a moment. Sure enough, it was a knock, after all. But she didn't dare get down to answer it. More knocks followed.

Through the noise of the storm we recognized Aunt's voice.

Mother sat bolt upright. "Be quick!" she told me.

It was Aunt indeed, soaked to the bone, without even a raincoat or umbrella. Her face was ghostly white, her shirt and pants muddied. Obviously, she had slipped and fallen.

Mother came down from the *kang*, a coat thrown over her shoulders. My brothers and sisters had all awakened by now, and we all looked at Aunt, dumbfounded.

"You — " Mother startled, "Why are you — "

Aunt just stood there stiffly, a waterlogged bundle weighing heavily in one arm. Rainwater streamed from her hair, shining against her pale cheeks and plastering her thin shirt against her breasts. A pool was rapidly forming around her muddy shoes. She looked steadily at Mother as if staring through a fog, her bright eyes enshrouded with mist.

"Sister — let me stay with you again, will you?"

she stammered. Her lips were purple with the cold.

"Of course! Why ever not? But hurry and get out of those wet clothes." Mother grasped her free hand and pulled her into the room. She grabbed some of her own clothes out of a box in the inner room and brought them back with some pillows and an armful of quilts.

We listened from the inner room as Mother asked her in a low voice what was going on. "Did you quarrel with your roommate?"

Aunt only sobbed the word "Sister."

"A twenty-year-old girl must learn to be broadminded. Living in a collective dorm is not the same as living at home, you know."

Though Aunt's sobbing was soft and low, it broke my heart.

That night, Mother slept in the outer room with Aunt.

The following day Aunt fell sick. In her fever, she murmured something incomprehensible.

On the third day, Mother stood before the bed, looking thoughtfully at Aunt, who was still in a deep sleep. Mother took up a rag and absently dusted here and there. Then suddenly she seemed to make her mind up. "Shaosheng," she said, "stay here and watch over your aunt. I'm going to fetch the traditional doctor from the private clinic."

She was back with the doctor in just a few moments. Seeing us clustered around the bed, she flared up. "Out with you! Why are you hanging around here?" Her voice had an accusatory tone that seemed quite unreasonable. I could tell she was greatly troubled, and I trotted out obediently.

We didn't feel it was safe to come back in even after the doctor left. We peered stealthily through the half-buried window. Mother knelt beside the bed holding Aunt's shoulder with one hand and a cup in the other. Commandingly she spoke, "Brown sugar water, drink it."

Aunt rose feebly and downed the contents of the cup. Mother helped her lie back down, then sat along the bed. Looking her square in the face, she said coldly, "Your factory leaders have been here, did you know that?"

Aunt's head seemed to give a weak shake against the pillow. She looked back at Mother, shamefaced as a criminal under interrogation.

"How far gone?"

"Three months."

"You cheated me!"

Aunt did not speak.

"You escaped my eyes, but did you think you could manage to escape the eyes of everyone else? How long did you think you could hide it?"

Aunt did not answer.

"Tell me, whose is it?"

" .... "

"Speak!"

Not a word from Aunt.

"Are you dumb?"

"I can't tell you, Sister. I will tell no one."

"You—" Mother had grown very angry, and stood up suddenly. But she contained her rage and sat down again. "All right, I won't press you for the name of this respectable person. But since things have gone this far, why don't you get married?"

Aunt did not respond.

"He — has he deserted you?"

Again, Aunt's head quivered against the pillow.

"Then, can it be that you don't wish to marry?"

Silence.

"Speak to me!"

"I can't get married to him —"

"What? You're carrying his child, yet you say you can't marry him?"

"Sister, please — don't press me any more." Two large tears rolled down her cheeks as she closed her eyes.

"But I will, I will ask until this is clear to me. Your father left you in my care, or have you forgotten?" Mother's anger was back full force. "If you can't tell me, you can leave this house. I won't have people pointing at me and whispering behind my back that I'm harbouring a girl who's carrying a baby that comes from nowhere!"

Aunt opened her eyes and looked back at Mother through her tears. "Don't worry — I will go as soon as I'm well enough. I'll go. Not for the world would I ruin your good name."

"Go? And suppose you tell me where you mean to go?"

"If there is nowhere else to go, there is always death." She hid her face in the quilt, which still shook lightly.

Drawing a heavy sigh, Mother said with pity and reproach, "You, you ... why did you have to do this? How could you let this happen?" Lifting a corner of the quilt, she wiped the tears from Aunt's face.

Aunt still would not tell who the father was.

She was fired by the factory.

Mother didn't throw her out into the street.

In our home, Aunt gave birth to a baby girl.

When the baby was one month old, Aunt's father came from the village to take them both back there. Mother's voice quavered with guilt when she said to him, "Uncle, I have failed. I didn't live up to your trust."

Cradling her baby in her arms, Aunt moved step by step toward Mother and then sank to her knees. She looked up at her, face wet with tears. Her lips moved as though she longed to speak, but she could not utter a syllable.

Mother reached down and helped her to her feet. Her lips were quivering, too, but she couldn't say a word.

Mother turned and went into the room, where she remained the rest of that day.

I saw the sad trio to the railway station. As I stood and watched the train move further and further into the distance, I felt as if it were carrying away the most beautiful thing in my heart.

Back home, I saw my mother's eyes were red from weeping.

Not long after she left, Aunt wrote to tell us she might be offered a teaching position at her village school. Mother and I felt a little relieved. But a few months later, another letter said that the teaching job had been out of the question.

As the years passed, we had no chances for reunion. All we had were just letters coming and going.

The year I went to junior high school, Aunt brought

her child and stayed with us for a couple of weeks. The baby by then was five years old. She could speak — in fact, she had a very pleasing tongue. But she was very pale and skinny. Mother loved this fatherless child devotedly. If she had any delicious tidbit, she would keep it for her. This was during the catastrophic years of the 1960s, so of course there really were no treats to eat — even mixed flour buns could make one's mouth water.

Aunt had aged dramatically; she looked like a woman in her thirties. Her clothes were patched and her face was etched with lines of worry. In two weeks I almost never saw her smile.

Mother had in private tried to talk her into looking for a man.

Looking at her child, Aunt had answered sadly, "I am not in the mood for man-hunting. I'll wait until the child grows up."

Mother told her not to be a fool. "What man is going to have you then? You shouldn't waste any time. Find a husband while you're still young. He can help you raise the child."

Aunt kept quiet for a while, then said in a soft voice, "I'm afraid of marrying a stepfather with no real feeling for her — the child could be maltreated."

Mother's temper flared. "So who's her blood father, then? If he's a man of such tremendous conscience, how is it he deserted you and his daughter as he did? "

"Please — don't think of him that way— " She almost seemed to beg.

Mother bit back much she had to say.

Life in those years was hard for us, too, and Aunt

couldn't bring herself to take a share of what slight food we had. She returned to the village after two weeks.

Twenty-three years passed since that visit. I left high school and was sent to the country. Then I went to university, and finally settled in Beijing. I had never seen my aunt since.

As I looked back over the past, I was filled with compassion for my aunt, and swept with hatred for the man who had lived in her heart for such a fleeting instant, then apparently vanished from the earth. He was the author of her miserable existence.

I had gone from Harbin to labour in the Great Northern Wildnerness; from there to Shanghai, then to Beijing. I had nearly forgotten this aunt during all the twists and turns of the road of my life. Only the letters in which my brothers and sisters mentioned her reminded me of this woman, who though not related to me by blood, had been as dear as my mother to me. The thought of her brought back her image as she knelt in front of Mother, her face pale and tearstained, her month-old infant in her arms. When she left, she left me with an impression and an influence far too deep to fade entirely. Hearing now that she hadn't long to live, I missed her all the more poignantly.

The next day, I left early in the morning and caught the train to Double-Town.

The village was a large one, consisting of over a hundred households. Many of them lived in new brick dwellings, and even the courtyard walls were built of brick. This was proof enough that the peasants were much better off.

I asked several villagers where Aunt lived, but they all shook their heads and said they knew no one of that description. At last, though, a young girl hearing Aunt's name exclaimed, "It's Xiuxiu's mother that you're looking for!" She volunteered to show me the way.

As we walked, she asked me, "Are you from Tianjin?"

"What makes you think I'm from Tianjin?" I wondered.

"Xiuxiu is studying at a university in Tianjin," the girl replied. "Are you in her class?" Conjecture lit her eyes.

"I am from Harbin. Xiuxiu is my cousin, and her mother is my aunt."

"Is that so? I've never heard about this before," the girl pondered, as the conjecture became an out-and-out search. She looked me up and down as if she thought she might be able to see through me.

At last she led me into a shabby courtyard, announcing, "Here we are!" The dilapidated old house, presented a sharp contrast with the newer surrounding it.

I hesitated before entering.

A middle-aged woman boiling herbal medicine by the *kang* turned round in surprise and asked, "Who are you looking for?"

"I've come here from Harbin to see my aunt."

"Ah, come in, come in ... I know who you are. She talks about you every day."

I ducked into the inner room, and there was my aunt, lying limply on the *kang*. She did indeed seem near death. Her eyes widened when she looked at me.

"Aunt!" I cried involuntarily.

"Is it Shaosheng?" She struggled to sit up, but was unable to. I hurried to her and gently held her quilt to keep her from trying again.

She took my hand in hers, and her eyes began to brim with tears. "I didn't think that I would be able to see you again," she said.

I turned to thank the neighbour woman, whom the villagers had entrusted with Aunt's care, and she went out, leaving us alone.

Aunt patted the edge of the *kang*. Her hand looked dark and shrivelled, and the skin had grown rough. Her arm lay against the bedding like a lifeless limb, and she could hardly lift her hand. She seemed unable to move her wrist, only her stiffly bent finger moved up, and then dropped. I thought about how tenderly that hand once had touched me, and with what love.

Possibly only I could understand her weak gesture. I moved to the *kang* and sat down beside her.

She grasped my hand, and held it so tightly it seemed she would expend the last of her strength with that grasp. It was as if she held life with her hand. She was like a child who holds tight to its mother before being left alone.

My heart felt large with grief.

I watched her face, searching for the memory of my childhood, looking for the beauty I remembered, even a fragment of that beauty. This was the face before which I learned what shame was, the face of the woman who made me understand loveliness when I was just a little boy. I could scarcely recognize that face, so old had it become, so waxy, grey, so swollen. Her eyes were spiritless, her hair lank and thin And she was but a few years past forty!

"Do I ... do I look very ugly?" She spoke weakly, her almost-vacant eyes resting on my face.

"No, you mustn't talk like that. Soon you will be fine." I turned away. I couldn't look at her.

"Will I? Maybe ... I don't think I'm going to die like this." She smiled, and that smile was like a flash of sunlight against a withered leaf.

A few hens marched into the room like the masters of the house, scratching here and picking there as if no one else were present.

"Will you feed the chickens for me? There's rice in the grain box in the outer room."

I stood up and called the hens out into the courtyard. Spreading the rice mechanically, I thought about the man hidden in the shadows behind Aunt's tragic fate. Somehow I felt sinful for being a man.

Just then there was a sudden clamour of movement inside the house. I rushed in to find Aunt lying in a heap, and water spilled all over the floor. A towel and a cake of soap lay in the puddle, and the basin had rolled into the corner.

I moved quickly to help her up and lift her onto the *kang*. She had lost so much weight. Her clothes were drenched. She still clutched the towel.

"I must look ... so ugly ... I want to wash ... my face, and my hair ..." I could detect a blush from shame on the grey face. The woman's pride shook me violently. Ah! My aunt!

I could not find words, so confused were my thoughts and emotions at that moment. In silence I retrieved the basin and soap and picked up the shards of her little mirror.

After refilling the basin with warm water, I set it at the edge of the *kang*. Resting her head on my knees, I wordlessly washed the face and the hair of this woman, whom I had loved and respected so profoundly when I was a child. I was trying to repay her in some way. Yet I knew my repayment was hardly worth the mentioning. The tears that rolled from the corners of her eyes as I bathed her were matched by my own.

When I sat back again and looked at her, she reached for my hand and spoke gently, "Do you ... want to listen?"

"What do you have to tell me?"

"The thing that happened in that year."

Not sure of what to say, I simply nodded my head.

"I was once in love," she began. In her voice I heard a calmness, even happiness, I was hard put to understand.

"I was once in love," she said again. "I know you, your mother, your whole family —— even my daughter Xiuxiu —— you all hate him; you hate the man I loved. But I don't hate him. I don't hate him in the least. How I loved him! And how he loved me, too." Her voice was growing stronger, and to my surprise, it didn't break as she went on.

"He loved me whole-heartedly, so deeply that I knew I would be fulfilled even if I died. Since you're grown-up now, you must know how entirely a man and a woman can love each other. He had been a soldier, had gone to war and had won a second-class merit citation. Then he became a probationary Party member, and was the leader of the women workers. Everyone agreed that he was a man of fine character. Even your mother would have agreed how fine a man he was, if she had only met him.

"At that time we were like two children. We didn't tell your mother we were in love. First, we didn't want her to fuss and worry about our wedding, and second —— I wanted to surprise her. So we decided we would marry privately, and then go and see her afterwards. That way she would have all of the happiness to share, and none of the trouble of planning and arranging a wedding. We were really so childlike! We kept our love a secret, not only from your mother, but from everyone. We met in private, we loved as if isolated from the rest of the world.

"He was part of the crew that fought the flood. At Mid-Autumn Festival, all my roommates went home to their families, and I was left alone. I felt terribly lonely. But he appeared at my door, and I was more delighted at the sight of him than I can tell you. I wished that we could spend the day together, but he said he had to go back to work against the flood.

"'Weren't you out there on the last shift?' I said. 'You shouldn't have to go this time!'

"'Don't forget that I'm a probationary Party member,' he reminded me. I was a little annoyed, and said I didn't think he had me in his heart at all. But he kept his temper, and smiled at me with such good nature I couldn't bear to be angry with him. This man was not the sort to talk a lot, and he didn't gush over me with sweet phrases like 'How I adore you!' But I knew. I understand how much he loved me —— I was the only woman in the whole of his heart. Your mother was right when she told me that nobody else but a woman in love knows when a man truly loves her. And I knew how completely he cared for me.

"I saw a button was missing from his coat. I looked around and found another one, and wanted to sew it on for him. He didn't want me to, but I insisted. Oh, you can't imagine how tall he was! I was like a child as I stood before him. At that moment I was lost in happiness. But before I had sewn more than a couple of stitches, we heard the clanging of the gongs, and voices calling —— 'The flood crews will be off at once! The trucks won't wait a single minute!'

"As soon as he heard, he pulled off the half-sewn button and pressed it into my hand. He was about to rush out the door but I caught him by the sleeve, picked up two moon cakes and put them into his pockets. He kissed me and then stepped out the door.

"If anyone could love me with all his heart, for all my life, it had to be him. Until I fell in love with him, I had never felt close to a man. And I have loved only this man, all my life.

"Because I knew that soon I would be his wife and he my husband, I had given myself to him. I felt no shame about that. But that night, as he tried to stop the break in the dam, he was drowned. I heard people say that the two moon cakes were found in his pockets, untouched.

"He was honoured as a martyr, and admitted posthumously as a member of the Party. A memorial service was held for him at the factory. Many people wept bitterly, and many said they wanted to learn from his example. His photograph appeared in the paper, with stories of his deeds. On the day they unveiled the monument to the flood resistance, the mayor said his name would live forever, in the hearts of his fellow citizens.

"I couldn't keep from crying until my eyes were swollen. But so many others were weeping, too — nobody guessed that my grief was more personal, that I was three months pregnant with his child. Standing there among them, I vowed that I would never tell a soul whose child it was."

Here she stopped, and stared up at the ceiling. Her face remained almost expressionless, as if she were a statue. She had told her story steadily, as if she had repeated it many times to herself. She had murmured words of the most intimate possible emotions, and I thought it must have been the very strength of those emotions that strengthened her, that made it possible for her to tell her story though she seemed about to breathe her last.

We both were lost in thought. Like a fish in the silence, my soul sank into dark cold depths, then drifted up again as if to bask in the warmth and light of the sun shining through the ripples. I was not sure of fantasy or of reality.

I felt the grief of someone mourning the passing of a dearest one.

She opened her mouth at last. "If it happened today, and I were what I was then, perhaps I wouldn't try to keep it from people. But at that time, I couldn't speak. How could I? He lóved me, and I loved him so ... I couldn't let him down. Will you ... open that box?"

I stood up and opened an old box at one corner of the *kang*.

"Take out that small tin box, and give it to me."

It was a turner's tool kit. I held it in my hands and handed it to her.

She took a key from her wrist and opened the box.

"Just take a look— " Her look was telling, "I was not cheating you, not a single word was false."

In the metal box I found a folded piece of yellowed newsprint. Wrapped up in it was a black button, with a bit of thread.

"For many years, so many people tried to make me tell. But I didn't say a word. Now when no one asked I felt the urge to tell someone, and let this man understand. Why? I have kept it so many years. And I don't know what's wrong with me."

"Tomorrow I am taking you back to Harbin," I told her. "My mother misses you so, my brothers and sisters, everyone misses you."

"Harbin ..." Her face lit up. "I miss the family, too. Tomorrow...."

Loudly I said, "Tomorrow, yes."

"Good." She smiled, and said softly, "I didn't tell Xiuxiu of my illness. She's preparing for the post-graduate entrance examinations. I didn't want her to be distracted, it would ruin her future. Beijing is close to Tianjin. I will leave her in your care...."

Again I felt near to tears. But it had been so many years since I had cried. It wasn't that my heart had grown numb. So, I had simply buried all dreams and emotions in my heart. I had grown accustomed to restraint; not crying was my habit.

But how I wanted to cry that day.

In the darkness I sat up very late with Aunt. Then I went to sleep in the other room. As I sat with her, I thought she was aware of my presence, but she didn't speak to me again. She just held onto my hand gently, eyes closed, an almost beatific smile lingering on her face.

The next morning she died. But that look of contentment remained on her face, a peaceful look, a look of no regret.

I took the black button back to Beijing.

I put it in my wife's small ring box, and we placed it on the bookshelf, where I can always look at it and think of my aunt. I know that I will treasure it forever, and that I will never open that delicate box, nor will I ever show to anybody that black button.

Translated by Liu Shicong and Christine Ferreira

Ice Dam

"DAD, look!"

"My God — "

Zhai Laosong was thunderstruck — behind the damp veil of the early morning mist, in the gorge between the left and right ridges of Kuishan Mountain, a towering silvery dam had appeared, like a precipice rearing high out of nowhere or lofty battlements soaring skywards, blocking out the part of the sky where the sun normally hung at this time of the morning over Zhaicun Village.

"Dad, what is it?"

"An ice ... an ice dam."

"What's an ice dam, dad?"

Silence.

"It wasn't there when we came up last night!"

Silence.

Zhai Laosong was rooted to the ground in awe. He wanted to drag his son away from the place, but his legs were jelly.

All around was an eerie silence.

The ice dam gave off a mysterious pale blue light.

The original feeling of surprise suddenly gave way to one of gut-wrenching terror. Zhai Laosong, who had never known fright before in his life, felt his heart throb with fear. Subconsciously, he lowered his gun from his shoulder, as though suddenly confronted with a bear.

The hares dangling from the barrel of his gun fell to the soft snow-covered ground.

"Dad, you — "

"Run back and fetch your brother-in-law!"

As he spoke, his old eyes, buried beneath the fox-fur hat that reached down to his eyebrows, stared with unusual intensity at the seemingly impregnable cliff that was the ice dam. The trembling fear in his voice infected his son. His faithful hunting dog stuck his black nose in the air and started sniffing and whining; it was as though he could smell a deadly presence nearby. His ears pricked up and he started to growl.

"Dad, is it very important?"

"Run back, will you?!"

His son took to his heels.

The terror was like a huge fist, bearing down with all its might on the old hunter, flattening him.

He sat down on the snow.

Even thicker fog was seeping out from the wood. It floated over, and the ice dam appeared, fantastically, to recede gradually.

He rubbed his eyes and listened carefully. It actually wasn't all that quiet. Faint noises came through the thick milky fog intermittently.

It was the sort of muffled cracking a skyscraper would make as it collapsed slowly.

The sound made him shudder with fear.

His dog suddenly started barking angrily and then plunged in frenzy toward the dangerous veil of fog.

"Saihu, come back!"

He did not come back.

Zhai Laosong quickly pressed a bullet into the bore of the gun and then, without even bothering to aim, shot down his beloved hunting dog. He saw the dog running wildly, then, as he leaped, his neck slumping, his body curling in mid-air, his hind legs swinging forward unimaginably, then dropping to the ground like a black fur collar, stretched straight out and lying there perfectly still.

"Saihu...."

He felt like dying.

He could not have allowed the dog to challenge the ice dam — the impact of a frog might have caused that towering edifice to collapse in a split second.

That's what he thought.

That's one of the dangers when an ice dam is suddenly formed.

Terror spread throughout his heart.

The thick fog drifted away and the ice dam reappeared. He could see it even more clearly now — layers of ice pressing down on more layers of ice, rows and rows of incredibly sharp fang-like spikes, white and interlocking. So magnificent at a first glance, so savage when you looked at it closely. Zhai Laosong seemed to feel the whole ice dam shudder and tremble slightly after the sound of the shot. In fact, it had not moved at all.

The early morning sunlight was like a tangerine-coloured liqueur whose stain crept from the ice dam to the two mountain ridges with its light, turning the ice dam resplendent green-gold with refracted rainbow-coloured rays, a rainbow of death, towering and perilous, magnificent and false. Up in the mouth of the gorge, the river was carrying countless barges of ice and piling them up to form a revenging and destructive power that would eventually burst forth. When the

river of ice flooded and crushed the land, nothing
would remain for miles around....

Miles around were beyond his comprehension, but
there behind him was Zhaicun Village with upwards of
a thousand men, women and children in it!

How much longer would the ice dam hold?

Maybe it would collapse straight away, before his
son got back to the village.

God help me!

Buddha preserve us!

Zhai Laosong, who had never believed in spirits or
devils all his life, prayed devoutly for everyone in
Zhaicun Village, for himself and for his son.

He wanted to stand up, but found that not only
were his legs refusing to do his bidding, his whole
body seemed paralysed. He had heard the village elders
talk about the terrors of ice dams. The last one had
occurred during the nineteenth century, and had formed
up in the gorge that time too. The river had been cut
off and had piled up more and more blocks of ice until
the sun came out and the ice dam collapsed. The ice
had shovelled four or five villages off the face of the
earth. The colliding sheets of ice could slice through
human flesh as easily as a scythe, and could grind it
as easily as a human could grind a bean on a millstone. Afterwards, nothing even vaguely resembling a
human limb had been found. Flocks of crows
laboriously pecked here and there in the slurry, occasionally pulling out a beakful of flesh....

Poor Saihu. What a stupid way to die. Please
don't hate me.

Saihu, Saihu, maybe I'll die a crueller death than
you. Maybe a thousand villagers will die a crueller

death than you.

Crr ... crr ... err ... crack ... crr....

The bloodcurdling noise came clearer now. It was as though millions of teeth were gnawing ever harder behind the ice dam....

Crr ... crr ... crack....

Suddenly a huge jagged block of ice at the top of the ice dam was jolted by some force. The block of ice lurched forward until it was half in mid-air, half resting on the lip of the ice dam, rocking back and forth like a seesaw. Then it was jolted again and started turning over and over as it plummeted. With an almighty crash, it smashed completely, sending shards of crystal flying in all directions. The sky was filled with beautiful, glittering gems.

Zhai Laosong's heart leapt to his throat.

Glug ... glug....

The pent-up, freezing early spring water trickled obstinately over the lip of the ice dam. It dripped down over its precipitous face, washing its rows of sharp teeth, as though cleaning them for the feast of human flesh to come. The magnificent but deadly ice dam looked just like a colossal crocodile.

Glug ... glug....

Zhai Laosong watched the dam-level water carry a few huge blocks of ice as though they were nothing and piling them up on to the ice dam.

He remained there as though he had been turned to stone.

Oh my God....

His very soul started trembling.

He looked back and saw his fourteen-year-old son standing on the wooden bridge in front of the village, staring dumbly at him and not moving an inch. It must be because he shot the dog. Because his son had never heard the stories about the cruelty and destructiveness of ice dams, he was more shocked than scared. The ice dam was probably greater than anything he had imagined even in his wildest dreams.

Low-lying Zhaicun Village continued to sleep tranquilly. The smoke that would pour out of the chimneys when people were up was nowhere to be seen: the busy farming season would not be starting for another month, and it was now the "early to bed, late to rise" rutting season. At sunrise, couples all round the village were clasped together and lazily slipping back to sleep.

Zhai Laosong gesticulated at his son.

His son, however, just started walking back towards him.

Zhai Laosong was beside himself with anger.

"Run and get your brother-in-law or I'll shoot you too!"

He raised his gun menacingly at his son.

Not frightened, his son ran towards him.

"You brat!" He muttered to himself and pressed another bullet into the bore of the gun.

Bang!

His son froze in his tracks, terrified now, and turned round and stumbled as he waded at top speed through the deep snow back towards the village.

His father had actually just fired into space.

He struggled to his feet, controlling the terror inside him.

Looking at the ice dam he hesitated a moment, then slung his gun over his shoulder and started with measured strides towards the magnificent deadly silver dam. It was as though his gun was a sort of magic wand that would help him escape should the dam suddenly collapse.

He wanted to know whether the silver dam was really as fragile as he guessed or whether it was in fact quite solid —— because then the Zhaicun villagers would still be able to escape in time! Lord protect us, let's hope it's solid....

He crept cautiously towards the silvery dam, treading as lightly as he could. The snow crunched under his feet and he knew that with each step he was nearing a deadly danger disguised as a thing of majesty, and probably also a sudden, very messy death. But he did not stop because at the same time a solemn, sacred, unshirkable sense of mission was welling up in his heart. A sense of infinite mercy towards his fellow creatures; a pity for living things. Zhai Laosong, who had never experienced this kind of sentiment before, experienced it now. It was a force that sapped him of his own will, a force that made him act involuntarily. As soon as it sprouted in his breast he was totally subservient to it.

Although he hated much about Zhaicun Village, he was the village head and local Party secretary. Over half his life had been spent acting literally as a civil servant for the Zhaicun villagers. Even during the years of the "cultural revolution" he had gone all out to protect them from the rigours of "politics". If a few people had been hurt, this had been through no fault of his, rather that no matter how hard he had tried to protect them, in the end there had been nothing that he could do. However, not only did the villagers fail

to repay his kindness, last autumn they had even openly looted the orchard he had been tending just like ban-
dits. The three years of labour he had put into the orchard was all for nothing: he was left with nothing but
a debt of two thousand yuan. Luckily his daughter
Xiumei had got rich raising rabbits and was able to
bail him out, otherwise his only choice would have
been between hanging himself or cutting his throat....

The incident was brought to the attention of the
county court and the county Public Security Bureau.
The Public Security Bureau sent over a jeep and ar-
rested the ringleaders. The county court advised him to
sue, but he refused to do so.

When the looters were interrogated they were quite
frank: "Other people were looting. Do you think I'd
just stand by and watch? Of course I did the same!
I'd have been an idiot if I hadn't."

They all said the same thing in the same open way.
They did not feel in the least bit ashamed.

When the ringleaders were interrogated, they replied
with a question of their own: "Was it Zhai Laosong
that reported us? That old sod's got no idea of family
ties!"

Their interrogators replied truthfully that he had not
reported them yet.

Then they all laughed, even sneering at the court
people.

"If he didn't report us, what did you arrest us for?
What are you interrogating us for?"

Then they added: "That orchard used to be a public orchard, but when it was, it never produced any
fruit. Then Zhai Laosong comes along and not three
years later it starts producing fruit. Why shouldn't we

take from it?''

"If you want to say we ripped anybody off, then we ripped God off! Otherwise there's no justice in this world. And we were taking from family!''

They spoke plausibly and at great length and in a totally forthright manner. They felt no shame whatsoever.

The court decided that they were just "totally ignorant on legal issues". They felt as though they had been cruelly insulted and argued angrily that they weren't in the slightest bit "ignorant". They said that they at least understood general laws like the laws against robbing.

"You understand them and you robbed anyway?!''

The court officials were furious.

"We had to. Didn't we explain all that? We put a lot of sweat into that orchard too, but we didn't get anything out of it. We couldn't just let Zhai Laosong reap all the rewards. That wouldn't be fair!''

They were furious too.

The court decided that they were actually not "totally ignorant on legal issues" after all, they were just sly and tricky. The court asked Zhai Laosong to prosecute them as such, and they would punish them heavily.

"Release them. Release them and have done with it.''

Zhai Laosong just kept repeating the words blandly.

The officials were all perplexed. If he wasn't going to take them to court, then they would have to let them go free and the matter would be settled by being left unsettled.

In fact, there was a reason behind Zhai Laosong acting this way. He thought that if he went ahead and prosecuted, the court would certainly judge heavily against those relatives of his, and their wives and children would be disgraced too. With the loss of manpower, those families would find it hard to get by. If they were let off, he would have the prerogative of being able to look down upon them, despise them and hate them.

But Zhai Laosong had made a huge mistake. On the very same day that they were released, those relatives of his wreaked terrible damage on his orchard as a way of venting their anger, destroying a large number of trees. As if this was not enough, they then drove their pigs into the orchard and made them feast to their hearts' content on the fruit left on the ground that hadn't been stolen. Having vented their spleen, they went to find Zhai Laosong and said to him:

"Laosong, don't get angry ... we're not attacking you personally, it was just a matter of principle!"

"Laosong, we're getting richer day by day and you can too. But it has to be gradual: we can't have people getting rich like you did! If we hadn't taken your fruit you'd have got rich far too easily! Think about it. You'd have got rich far more easily than we could. Anyway, we only looted your orchard; we didn't steal anything from your house. We wouldn't do that ... you are family after all, and you are our elder."

They spoke in a forthright and sincere tone. They spoke in a pious tone. It was as though they were taking him into their confidence. They spoke with the conviction of people with easy consciences.

He snatched down the hunting rifle on the wall, wanting to massacre them all.

"Laosong, what are you doing?!"

"Laosong, you're a Party member! You were the village head! Do you mean to say you're not going to let us get away with ripping you off even once?"

He stared at them panic-stricken. He was so angry he was completely disorientated, momentarily losing sight of who was in the right and who was in the wrong.

They took advantage of his indecision to make good their escape.

From that moment onwards he gradually cut himself off from the village emotionally. Or maybe it would be just as fair to say that the village cut itself off from him. He would never do anything for the village anymore. He had once been a great optimist, expecting the lives of the Zhaicun villagers to improve day by day, with everyone becoming kinder and friendlier to each other as time went on; but the reality of Zhaicun village was just one long disappointment to him. The ties between the villagers were already less close than they had been in the past. Some of the villagers had not only got rich, they also cursed those who remained poor, gloating either openly or inwardly at their misfortunes.

Zhai Laosong had built himself a little shack up in the mountain forest, and he now avoided the village more and more, going to live in the shack with just his dog for company. He began to feel that he had become someone totally detached from the village and gradually got used to the idea. The Zhaicun villagers apparently grew to forget him too. Occasionally, when they heard the sound of his gun, they remembered that there had once been such a person as Zhai Laosong living in the village.

The Zhaicun villagers were all becoming better off. Zhai Laosong would often recall the events of ten, twenty or even thirty years ago. They had all been good people in those days, he thought. Poor but good. Kind, rich in sympathy and willing to help each other out. But now they had all turned bad to greater or lesser degrees, changing so that he felt himself a stranger to them and hated them.

His son-in-law — the present local Party secretary and head of Zhaicun village — would not agree with him on this point at any price. According to him, the villagers had not been so nice in the past either, being hostile towards culture and cultured people, believing that if they could appear to everyone as honest and hearty old peasants, then they had reached the pinnacle of human achievement. Moreover, they had been extremely docile, to the point of slavishness. The reason for this could be traced back to deep and lasting influences closely connected to the ancestral tradition. If a man in his fifties met a man in his twenties, the fact that the former's position in the clan hierarchy was far below that of the latter's would have made him adopt an ultra-respectful and quite insincere pose quite sickening to behold. According to Maosheng, the Zhaicun villagers were now passing through the tunnel from poverty to wealth, and so it was unreasonable to start reproaching them if they were turning sly in many respects. With their respective outlooks so completely at odds, father-in-law and son-in-law had very little to say to each other, and it was therefore only rarely that Laosong crossed his daughter's threshold....

The ice dam sloped inwards from top to bottom, looking like an inverted top hat. Zhai Laosong looked up but couldn't see the top of it. The teeth-like jagged edges and the needle-like points of the ice sheets were like a craggy layered cliff pressing down on his head. Cold water seeped through the cracks between the layers of ice, and behind the ice dam the cracking noise that had frightened him so badly came as a muffled rumble. It sounded like a million huge boulders bubbling away in a huge cauldron, crashing against each other as they tumbled about. One wave after another of the river water flooded over the lip of the ice dam, coming in a torrential downpour that soaked through his jacket in no time at all. However, staying directly under the ice dam did not frighten him nearly as much. He even dared to jot it with his gun.

Although it looked extremely threatening, it did not move a fraction.

Suddenly another block of ice the size of a small house was pushed over by the tempestuous river water surging behind the ice dam. It smashed countless protruding blocks of ice as it tipped over and then fell to the ground with an almighty crash. The bottom half of it was smashed to powder, and the top half leaned against the ice dam like a door, shutting Zhai Laosong behind it in a hollow. The crystalline shards and fragments of ice piled up into a big heap as though they were trying to bury him alive. As he climbed his way out, he looked like a badger clawing its way out of its blocked set. Laosong's legs were cut, but he had not dropped his gun. Freezing water dripped down from his collar and soaked his underclothes, making him shake with cold. He could not tell whether the ice dam would collapse in ten or twenty minutes, half an hour or an hour's time ... that was in the lap of the gods.

"Dad! What are you doing, dad?" his son yelled to him, standing on a large black rock by the river bed.

"Your brother-in-law —— where's your brother-in-law?"

Desperate, he limped over to his son.

"He's not at home!"

As he spoke, his son jumped down from the rock and started interrogating him: "What did you go and kill Saihu for?"

"Why isn't he at home?"

"How should I know? The door wasn't locked, and the *kang* hadn't been slept on. God knows where he's got to! Why did you kill Saihu?!"

Zhai Laosong did not pursue his questioning. What God knew he had known for a long time too.

He swore viciously: "That bastard!"

"You killed him for no reason whatsoever! That's the last time I go hunting with you!" His son reproached him angrily and then ran off towards the ice dam, as though he would have nothing more to do with him ever again.

"What are you trying to do?"

"I'm going to climb it!"

"Are you trying to get killed or something? Come back here!"

"Get lost!"

His son rebuffed him, climbing monkey-like up the jagged layers of ice.

Zhai Laosong rushed over and grabbed his son by the foot, bringing him down and crashing to the ground with him.

He jumped up and belted his son round the face.

"A whisker away from death and you're still mucking about!"

Dragging his son, he limped back to the village as fast as he could....

"You've got to go...."

"Don't move...."

He hugged her buxom body closer to him, nibbling at her earlobes and whispering, "You want to get rid of me or something? I'm staying until it's light."

"Didn't you hear the gun?"

"Mmm."

"That means he's in the village."

"So what? He's got his home, and I've got mine. We each mind our own business!"

"Aren't you worried about him finding out?"

"No."

She snuggled downwards and pressed her face against his chest. She giggled and then said lovingly, "Of course I don't want you to leave. I'm just worried someone'll see you...."

"Even if they do see me, so what?"

"I don't care."

"If you don't care, who does?"

"You do."

"Me?! Ha!"

"Yes, you! Mister village head, mister local Party secretary. You, with that Women's Federation county representative wife of yours. You've certainly got reason to be scared! You're scared of people gossiping behind your back, of being punished by the Party, of losing your reputation...."

As she spoke, she prodded him in the stomach.

He'd been feeling extremely amorous, but her words quenched his fire completely.

"Okay, okay, I'm scared then! I'm going now...."

He pulled away from her, pushed back the quilt and sat up. He grabbed his clothes and started getting dressed silently.

"Are you cross?" she asked anxiously, her beautiful phoenix eyes looking at him affectionately.

"No. What have I got to be angry about?"

"You are angry! I'm not having you leaving me in a bad mood...."

She was almost begging him.

He laughed a bitter laugh and took off the underclothes he had just this minute put on. He dived under the quilt and pulled her soft warm body towards him again. He started to fondle her, and she snuggled up to him, cat-like, her shapely eyes half closed, her pupils dilated and exuding love. She lay there enjoying his caresses and whispering the words she knew would make him happy....

They forgot themselves again and abandoned themselves to the pleasures of the moment.

The greatest regret in Zhai Maosheng's life was that this woman now resting in his arms had not become his wife. He had told the woman, whose name was Qianzi, that it was something that would always leave him angry and inconsolable. When she had heard, the tears had fallen like rain as she felt a mixture of joy and despair. She had choked with sobs.

He was more than willing to risk the condemnation of the village for the sake of this woman. In Zhaicun Village's history there had never been any scandal of

love affairs or adulterous goings-on. At least, such goings-on had never been discovered. Maosheng despised
this lilywhite tradition and bore it a vicious, albeit con-
cealed, animosity. Whereas he had never daringly pro-
claimed or revealed his hatred, any opportunity that he
got to secretly profane the tradition afforded him the satisfaction of a kind of revenge.

He could never break away from this woman he was
now embracing lovingly. This young local Party secretary denounced his immoral activities and then indulged
in them again; but he never felt guilty, because this
young widow Qianzi needed him too badly. He used
her the same way a camel uses a luxuriant patch of
grass. Only when he was wrapped up and melting in
her exuberant lust did he really feel like a
man — that he had not been a man in vain. At
other times he was just the village head and the local
Party secretary. The husband of the county representative of the Women's Federation. The son-in-law of the
man who had been cold-shouldered and denied the
Zhaicun villagers' common respect, Zhai Laosong.
That was all there was to it. That and nothing more.

Twenty-nine-year-old   Maosheng   and   twenty-
seven-year-old Qianzi had both been students of the
first county senior middle school. This was the only
"higher seat of learning" in the whole county, and
its graduates were all thought of as intellectuals. A few
years before, in the years when money had still not
completely wiped the floor with education, this had
been especially the case. More than just because they
were in their prime, the reason that the present head of
the county and the present secretary of the county
Party committee had been pulled up to leadership level

as intellectual cadres was that they held diplomas from the county senior middle school. It was rumoured that they had been very mediocre students too. Even now that the county had set up two new middle schools offering senior middle school courses, the first senior middle school was still the springboard that most literati dreaming of attending university would actually bounce from. Nowadays the higher middle school certificate was a grand, plastic-coated thing, but if you could not use it to get a notification of acceptance from a university, it was worthless compared with the plain card graduation certificate of twenty years ago.

In those years, when Maosheng and Qianzi came back to the village together for winter and summer holidays, the villagers invariably treated them as young prodigies. Even their elders would give them the fawning attention and respect due to future academics.

"Maosheng! Are you going to take the university entrance exams?"

"Of course I am!"

"Which university are you going for?"

"Qinghua! Or Beijing University maybe!"

"Which town are they?"

"Beijing of course!"

"Beijing ... ha ha! You're ambitious. That's good! The emperor's city!"

The villagers treated the complacent Maosheng with increased respect.

"What about you, Qianzi?"

Whenever she was asked, feeling a little embarrassed but full of confidence, Qianzi would reply: "The same as Maosheng!"

"Qinghua and Beijing universities?"

"Of course, if that's what Maosheng's going for!"

Her phoenix eyes would blink innocently, as though she was surprised that they should be asking her.

"It's great that you'll be together!"

The villagers were generous in their approval and encouragement for their joint ambition.

Their parents hoped even more keenly that such a day would soon become reality, and were even more considerate and loving towards them. They did not let them do any physical labour when the heavy farming season started for fear of exhausting their precious bodies. As for the two of them, they had never considered for one moment the fact that they might not get into university. The possibility was non-existent to them. In those years they just couldn't hold back their sky-high conceit and self-confidence. They were the two bright sparks in their class and their teachers' pride and joy. Even supposing only two students from the county got into university, who else could it be but them?

In those years, whenever they ate the freshly-cut village grain, their hearts would be flooded with a sort of nostalgia for their home. Standing there, bowl in hand, they already thought of themselves as not really belonging to Zhaicun Village anymore, and their only worry was that in the future it might not prove easy to get the chance to eat fresh hometown grain. The setting of Zhaicun might not be romantic, but the countryside certainly had its charms. On moonlit nights, among flowers, they would weave a bright future for themselves, a wonderful future, ambitious on a boundless scale and far beyond the wildest dreams of the wildest dreamer in the village.

"Qianzi...."

"Mmm?"

"Why is it that wherever I enter for an exam somewhere, you do too?"

"You know perfectly well!"

"Tell me!"

"No. Ask yourself!"

One still night, down by the bend in the river that
went round Zhaicun Village, under the little bridge that
looked like a pavilion on the water, Maosheng threw
off all his studently reserve and all pretence of refine-
ment and daringly started making teasing physical advances to her for the first time.

The morality of Zhaicun Village never allowed young
men and women to be together like this; there were
even taboos on brothers and sisters. However, in their
case the rigid and strict Zhaicun morality turned a
blind eye and left a hole in the net. In fact it was so tol-
erant that it would be no exaggeration to say that it
was "aiding and abetting" the evil.

The moonlight cast its glow over the river. The river
reflected Qianzi's beautiful image.

Restless and whimsical, Maosheng sat there sa-
vouring her delicate face in the mirror-like surface of the
water.

She hung her head and blushed, not saying a word.

Daringly, he laid her down on the mattress-like soft
grass on the bank....

If she had not moved from the daze of bewildered
pleasure to the realization that she had to fight out of
this perilous position, who knows what would have
happened...?

She pushed him away, covered her breast, and turned on him: "What's the big hurry? I'll be yours sooner or later!"

But that year he failed his exams, and she did too. After the first exam, which was a maths paper, they went over their answers together and discovered that they had both blundered on two big questions. They were naturally both panic-stricken. The next few papers proved even more of a disaster, and not only did their marks fall way short of those needed for Qinghua or Beijing University, they were not even anywhere near good enough to get them into the meanest provincial teachers' college.

The psychological makeup of the average Zhaicun Villager was very strange: it was very difficult to get hold of and very changeable. Their miserable failure in the exams was treated as a cause for celebration by many villagers; and their comeuppance made certain villagers happy for a very long time. The price that they paid for their previous arrogance and overconfidence left some villagers overwhelmed with glee, particularly the ones who had looked upon them as certainties to become lofty academics in Beijing, or the ones who had previously fawned on them and shown them tremendous respect. These villagers in particular now tried their hardest to drive the pair to their deaths through continuous sarcasm, mocking and humiliation. It was as though they were a pair of shameless frauds and as though all the fawning and respect represented an irreplaceable loss to those who had given it. God had eyes too and had served retribution out on a magnificent scale. Served the bastards right!

"Maosheng! Why haven't you gone yet?"

"Gone where, uncle?"

"Beijing University! Don't you want to go or something?"

Maosheng could only hang his head and shuffle away.

"Your ancestral tomb was just about to start billowing smoke.* What a pity the Earth God decided to shovel a load of earth over it to smother it out! Ha ha...!"

Words like this would pursue him as he left, accompanied by a bellow of laughter. This uncle of his, who shared the surname "Zhai", had apparently forgotten the fact that the two of them shared the same ancestors.

"Qianzi!"

"Mmm?"

"Come over here, I want to look at your hands!"

"What for, auntie?"

"I just want to look! Oh, just look at them ... they're so delicate and soft! So white ... and the fingers are so dainty. Those hands were made for wielding a writing brush ... it's a real shame that from now on they'll just be doing farmwork. It's enough to make you cry!"

"Auntie...."

Qianzi wanted to pull her hands away, but her aunt had them firmly gripped by the wrist.

"Qianzi. You have the heart of a lady, but you'll always be a slave girl. You said you wanted to go to uni-

---

*According to superstition, when black smoke appeared from an ancestral tomb it meant that the forefathers' descendents were on the verge of riches or officialdom.

versity so badly, but you failed your exams. It was predestined by fate.''

It sounded like sympathy, and the aunt's face
seemed to have sympathy written all over it; but sarcasm was lying just below the surface. The well-veiled
bitter laugh outlined by the wrinkle by her nose did
not escape the notice of the sensitive Qianzi.

"Auntie, let go of my hand!"

Qianzi blushed as bright as a beetroot, and her tears
started welling. She snatched her hands back and
turned to run towards the house....

"What are you crying for? What are you crying
for? Whose fault was it that you didn't get into university? Did someone put a curse on you or something?"

Mother scolded too.

The Zhaicun villagers had a widespread unspoken fear
of some dark horse suddenly springing to fame from
among people who had tilled the land for generations,
as though such an occurrence would be a catastrophe,
both harmful and dangerous to them. They could not
stand such a thing happening. But once someone was
commonly acknowledged as being important, they
would deify that person, treating him with the utmost
respect and reverence. If someone looked as though he
was going to be important and then fell just short,
then in the eyes of the villagers that person was not
even as good as an ordinary person. They would tram-
ple that person's self-respect underfoot and feel no guilt
whatsoever for doing so. Was it their fault if that person had tried to set himself up as important and
failed? Didn't that person deserve to be knocked down

a peg or two? They were not bad people. How often do peasants get the chance to snub anyone? The moment they got such an opportunity they naturally didn't want to let it slip by. They even thanked the good Lord for remembering them and giving them this one chance, so it was all perfectly justified.

As time went by, they did not mind seeing people getting wealthy — as long as their wealth did not come too easily. If people did get rich too easily they couldn't stand it, Zhai Laosong being a case in point. People who had made their fortunes through taking outrageous risks and who had suffered severe frustrations along the way they could abide and not feel too jealous of. They even grew to tolerate people who bedecked themselves with honorary titles, such as Maosheng's wife, the county representative of the Womens' Federation. Here the premise was that the titles were empty ones. If the person got some tangible benefit at the same time — a state cadre's salary or a chauffer-driven car for example — they would not put up with it at any price.

But they had a sort of instinctive dislike for scholars. They could sometimes pretend a respect for such people, but inside they hated them. They felt their sense of equality in intellectual matters coming under threat. In the future, remote Zhaicun Village, with its thousand or so souls, would not only be divided into rich and poor classes, but also those who had received higher education and those who had not, those with culture and those without — it was perfectly possible that they would also be divided into those whose later generations would be respected and whose would be despised. Just thinking about this was enough to make the villagers first depressed, and then furiously indignant. This then was the psychology of the Zhaicun villagers back then, and there is no reason to suppose that it has changed even today....

The two families' parents started placing Maosheng and Qianzi under close supervision, no longer allowing them opportunities to be together. The Zhaicun Village morality would no longer turn a blind eye. The net closed again.

One time, the repressed youth ran into Qianzi on her way to the family vegetable patch, a wicker basket on her arm.

"Qianzi, we can take the exams again next year!"

Qianzi turned away and refused to look at him, replying in a bleak voice: "I'm not taking the exams again. You do what you like!"

"Come on! If we stay in this village we'll never be treated as human beings!"

"If we failed again, I'd die!"

"We're bound to pass if we take them again."

"I'm not going to do it ... I'm scared."

Qianzi trudged away with her head low, not waiting to see if he had anything else to say....

At the start of the following year, Qianzi got married. Her husband was a cousin from a distant branch of the family and was called Guangyu.

Guangyu had just bought himself a walking tractor, and since he did a lot of private transportation work in the county town, money came very easily. Qianzi had not been willing and had made repeated suicide attempts, but unable to dissuade her parents, she ended up marrying him....

Maosheng hated her for a while and then stopped.

Next he hated her parents and all the Zhaicun villagers. Later still he hated nobody. Finally he ended up as Zhai Laosong's son-in-law. Zhai Laosong had felt honoured that his daughter's husband was the only senior middle-school graduate in the whole village. Maosheng felt no affection whatsoever for Zhai Laosong's daughter, Xiumei.

Three months after Maosheng married, Zhai Guangyu died in a traffic accident. Maosheng felt like dying himself: why couldn't he have waited just three months more to marry! Qianzi had turned from married woman to young widow, and maybe her parents would have agreed to her marrying him. Of all the women in the village, Qianzi was the only one he wanted.

Qianzi rued her fate even more bitterly. She would only be happy if she married Maosheng. Living with Guangyu had been impossible. Guangyu had been a chainsmoking drunkard, ignorant to the point of being unable to write the simplest note on his own. All he knew was how to earn money in big fistfuls and spend it like water. He would always choose dodgy characters for his friends too, inviting them round all the time to eat and make merry....

Why couldn't he have died three months earlier?

Maosheng's son was five years old now.

Qianzi had been a widow for six years.

Apart from Maosheng, none of the Zhaicun men attracted her in the least....

He kissed her, rested his head on her big breasts, and lay there quietly awhile. Then he let her go and said in a quiet voice: "I've really got to go. It's better if no one finds out...."

She would not let him go: "How long will your wife's meeting in town go on for?"

"Six or seven days."

"Will you come back tonight?"

"Do you want me too?"

"Yes." Her eyes sparkled. "I want you to come every night for the next six or seven days!"

"Then I'll come."

"Once when I saw your wife, and I tried to chat with her, she gave me a really funny look. Does she know anything?"

"She knows everything!"

"What, everything?"

"Yes. Apart from that we're together now."

"That's dreadful, surely?"

"If you do something, people always find out sooner or later. I dreamt about you one night and called out your name. I woke myself up with my own shouting and found her crying ... so I confessed everything about you and me...."

"What did she say?"

"She just cried. Before she left this time I asked her how many days she'd be gone. She just asked back: 'Would you like me to come back sooner or later?' I said: 'Sooner, of course!' She just made a face and said: 'Who are you trying to fool? The minute I'm gone you'll have the perfect opportunity. I'm taking our son with me this time in case you two find him an inconvenience!' Before she left she said to me: 'You long for Qianzi, and she longs for you. It's killing you, and I don't want you to die. If you died I'd be just another young widow, wouldn't I?'"

"Did she mean it?"

"With her ... who knows?"

"I feel like I'm really wronging her."

"I feel like I'm really wronging you. I can't divorce her ... I'm scared of going to court. I'm scared of them asking me: 'What is it about your wife that you don't like?' I wouldn't be able to answer. And I don't want my kid growing up to hate me either...."

She covered his mouth with her hand: "I don't blame you. Have I ever mentioned you getting divorced? I never have done, have I?"

He pulled her hands down from his mouth, held them in his and spoke haltingly: "But you ... I ... we can't carry on like this for ever!"

She sighed. There was a silence, and then she said quietly: "As long as you're your wife's man openly and my man secretly ... as long as half of you, or even just a part of you, is mine, I'll never complain...."

Hearing her talk like this, he sighed. He stretched out an arm from under the quilt, reached for his overcoat and fished out a cigarette.

The cigarette was really low quality, and he found puffing it difficult. He had to suck on it with all his might. She placed her snow-white arms on the pillow and rested her chin on them, giggling as she watched his efforts.

As he lay there puffing furiously, he thought guiltily about his wife, Xiumei. Xiumei was not at all beautiful, nor was she as dainty as a plum blossom.* Qianzi's body was like a mermaid's, luring him on.

---

* "Xiumei" means beautiful plum blossom.

Xiumei was a big clodhopper. Her legs were twice as thick as his. She was Zhai Laosong's daughter all right. Apart from her looks, however, Maosheng could really find nothing bad to say about her. She was very able. A few years ago she had started raising rabbits, and now there were over seven hundred of them. Their family's present prosperity was entirely due to those rabbits; and rabbit had paid for their new house too. He mustn't be quite completely ungrateful!

He thought back to himself and how he had joined the Party a few years ago. Before he joined, Zhai Laosong had sought him out and had a very serious chat with him: "Join the Party! You're the only intellectual in the whole village, so you've got to join. The Party needs intellectuals now!" This was in the days when he was not yet Zhai Laosong's son-in-law. Seeing how serious Zhai Laosong was, and how he was his elder, and how, representing the Party, he had taken the initiative to search him out, and how he had spoken so earnestly, Maosheng had felt he had no option but to fill in an application form to join up. Zhaicun Village had about ten Party members, and it was many a year since there had been any discussion of who could enter the Party. This was because in recent years no one had applied to join. The Party members were extremely surprised with Zhai Maosheng, thinking that for him to have an ambition like this in these days was very commendable. They were also very happy to have a little opportunity to show their existence as Party officials, something that had gradually been all but forgotten. Therefore they made no objection whatsoever to Maosheng joining the Party. Not long after Maosheng joined the Party, Zhai Laosong

abdicated, saying he was giving up his post to someone better qualified, and putting Maosheng's name forward for the post of local Party secretary. Again the
other members made no objection. The modern-day
— post of local Party secretary carried no power with it,
and Party members certainly didn't spend their days
racking their brains for schemes to get the post.
Today's local Party secretary only had jurisdiction
over Party matters. In a large village like this, non-
Party matters were many and needed someone to deal
with them as well. For example, in cases of wife beating, daughter-in-law bullying, people borrowing money
and not returning it etc., someone was needed to make
judgements and uphold public order. Therefore the
Zhaicun villagers generously put the official hat of village chief —— a position that had long existed in name
only —— on Zhai Maosheng's head too. The villagers
thought that holding two positions concurrently would
be tough on him, and so they passed a resolution to
give him a yearly supplement of one hundred yuan
"worry fee". This was yet another proof of the mag-
nanimity of Zhaicun villagers. One hundred yuan was
not, in his view, excessive for such a tough job. He de-
served it.

Qianzi raised herself slightly and fished out a packet
of cigarettes from the pocket of his jacket. She pulled
out a cigarette and rubbed it gently in her hands.
Thinking she wanted to smoke, he offered her some
matches. She shook her head, put the cigarette she had
softened back into the packet, pulled out another one
and started rubbing that too. Watching her so ab-
sorbed in this task on his behalf, a wave of tenderness
swamped him again.

"Guess how much money I've saved up," she said.

"It won't be much!"

"Don't underestimate me. Go on, guess!"

"I can't. How much?"

"Six thousand!" she replied proudly, "Three thousand in my savings account, and three thousand at home that I haven't had time to put in yet."

"That's not much."

"It's not bad!"

"It's nowhere near what Pockface Zhai's got!"

"No one can get near him. He's ganged up with a load of people round the county, and he's been flogging fake liquor and cigarettes, the old cheat!"

These last few years the Zhaicun villagers had been getting rich fast. Once the peasants had removed the fetters tying them to the land, they had relied on their own individual skills and got rich in their own way. Down by the village crossroads there were restaurants, hairdressers, cobblers, pancake sellers, soya milk sellers ... shops of all shapes and sizes stocking everything you needed. It was just like a small town. In matters of commerce, whereas it was true that Zhaicun villagers would rack their brains like mad to fleece as much money as possible from strangers, fellow villagers were not spared either. However, some were less vicious than others in their methods. Qianzi had sold the walking tractor that had been left to her when her husband died and had opened a smart little grocery to supply the whole village. She went about her business in a civilized way, and all the villagers became her customers. Since she would never make a fortune, no one bore her any secret grudge, and no one felt like teaching a lesson as they had to Zhai Laosong. Moreover, she made life easier for a lot of people.

Qianzi started chatting again: "I'd like to be able to expand the shop front, get in a few tables and bring in a cook from the town. What do you reckon?"

"If that's what you want to do, go right ahead!"

"I mean what I say."

"Well make up your mind, and when the time comes if you need any help, you just have to ask."

Suddenly there was a pounding at the door.

"Maosheng! Maosheng!"

The sonorous accents were evidently those of Zhai Laosong.

The two stared at each other dumbly a moment, not daring to breathe.

"Maosheng! Get your arse out here!"

In his panic, Maosheng tried to pull his shirt over his legs.

"Don't worry!"

Qianzi tugged his clothes off, shoved him his trousers, calmed herself down and called out in a sleepy sounding voice: "Who is it?"

"Me! Laosong! Are you deaf or something? Open the door quick!"

"I haven't got out of bed yet. What's the matter?"

Qianzi started getting dressed with an unusual calm. Seeing the panic-stricken Maosheng she hissed: "What are you so scared about? You've got me to protect you!"

"Hurry up and make Maosheng come out!"

Bang! Bang! Bang!

Zhai Laosong was using the butt of his rifle to

pound the door.

Indoors, Qianzi raised her voice: "What are you doing looking for your son-in-law round here at this hour of the morning? You must be drunk. Did you think you'd come and make trouble? Well, you'd better not try any of that with me!"

"Don't give me that! If you don't open the door, I'll smash in the window!"

Zhai Laosong moved round to the window.

A bell started ringing out.

Bong! Bong! Bong!

Maosheng was pale with fright. He thought that Zhai Laosong was gathering all the villagers together to witness his adultery.

"Qianzi, shall I sneak out the back?"

"I boarded up the back door!"

"Oh no!"

Maosheng was hopping from foot to foot.

"We're both fully dressed: what are you worried about? Go and sit by the table like a civilized person!" Qianzi fished out an abacus and an account book, placed them on the table together with a pile of receipts and said to Maosheng, "Just say you spent the night helping me do my accounts!" Then she quickly rolled up the quilt, not forgetting to yell back at Laosong as she did so: "Go on then if you're so brave! Smash my window!"

Qianzi too was sure Zhai Laosong was going to expose their adultery in front of the villagers, but she stayed very calm up to this point. Her own parents had both died two years ago, and as she had no relatives to worry about, nothing scared her.

"Are you opening that door or not?"

"No!"

She replied recklessly, meeting force with force.

"If I've been here helping you do your accounts, you'd better open up," whispered Maosheng.

Maosheng was now a lot calmer than he had been a couple of seconds ago. He had just decided that if anyone harmed the slightest hair on Qianzi's head, he would fight them to the death. Including his father-in-law. He decided to brazen it out too. Realizing that what Maosheng said made a lot of sense, Qianzi was about to open the door. However, Zhai Laosong couldn't control himself a moment longer in his fury, and with an almighty crash the pane of glass was shattered. Next the window frame was smashed open with Zhai Laosong's rifle butt, and his furious face appeared at the window. He leapt through the window into the room, landing on the *kang* and trampling over the red silk quilt with his wet and muddy boots.

"I ... I was helping Qianzi do her accounts...."

Maosheng jumped up and shoved Qianzi behind him. As he spoke, he grabbed the iron-framed abacus defensively, preparing to use it as a weapon if the need arose.

Zhai Laosong's face took on an awful expression of anger, and jumping down from the *kang*, he strode over to Maosheng and gave him a vicious crack across the face that almost sent him sprawling.

Qianzi pushed the local Party secretary gently to one side and stepped forward herself. She stood in front of the once respected village chief, put her hands on her hips and gave a sneer: "Don't hit your son-in-law. Hit me. I seduced him."

Zhai Laosong's cheeks trembled with rage, and he

was robbed of speech.

"Don't you dare? You've got a shotgun, haven't you? She opened the front of her gown, revealing a maroon embroidered bra: "Shoot me then. Haven't you got the guts? Are you scared of the law catching up with you? If you're not going to do it, then just bugger off! I hate you! You were Guangyu's matchmaker. How much did he give you? And it was you who told my parents that according to my position in the clan I should have been Maosheng's aunt, and so I couldn't marry him no matter what! What did you say it for? Why don't you let me take a look at that family tree of yours? Maybe it says I'm your aunt."

With her having been widowed for quite a few years and having run a grocery for a long while too, most of Qianzi's gentleness had long since worn off. Life had made her a lot bolder.

"Why, you...!"

Zhai Laosong raised his fist as if to strike her, but Qianzi stood firm and didn't even bat an eyelid. She stared at him coldly, and he realized suddenly that this was not a woman that you could hit lightly. He grabbed her by the arm and pulled her out of the way, then pointed at his son-in-law and yelled: "Listen, you! An ice dam has formed up in the pass. Get all the villagers together, then head for the mountains!"

Hearing something completely different to what he was expecting, Maosheng was thrown off balance. Trying to get hold of himself, he asked incomprehendingly, "Ice dam? What ice dam?"

The bell was still ringing. Bong! Bong! Bong!

"A load of ice has piled up in the pass, blocking off the river. It's about six or seven storeys high! The river's almost risen as high as the ice dam already. The minute the dam collapses, this village is finished! The villagers won't take any notice of the bell, so you and me are going to go from door to door to tell them to run for their lives! Let's hope we're not too late!''

As Zhai Laosong spoke, he could see his son-in-law was only half convinced. He didn't say anything else, just dragged him outside.

A woman's purple face was viewing the scene indifferently over the courtyard wall. It was Pockface Zhai's wife.

"You!" Zhai Laosong pointed at her. "Get indoors, wake everyone up, then run for your life!''

The woman stood there, aloof and indifferent.

Zhai Laosong couldn't be bothered with her. He dragged his son-in-law up on to the roof of Qianzi's chicken coop and then on to the roof of her house.

Maosheng finally saw with his own eyes the towering silvery ice dam rearing up in the pass. The fiery red disc of sun had just shown its face from behind the dam, and the morning mist had now completely dispersed. In the rays of the sun, the ice dam looked as though it was bleeding.

Qianzi had followed them out into the courtyard too. She looked up at the two of them on the roof.

"Qianzi!" Pockface Zhai's wife put on a false smile and struck up a conversation with her. "Is Maosheng's wife off in town again?''

Qianzi did not bother to reply. She grabbed a hen that had been startled out of the coop and threw it in the direction of the courtyard wall: "Get back to your coop, you revolting creature!''

The hen just missed the woman's head. The woman

gave a scream, and her purple face immediately disappeared from the wall.

At the same moment, Zhai Laosong and Maosheng jumped down from the roof.

"I'll go to the office and broadcast a message to get everyone up the mountain!" said Maosheng, and then he ran off as fast as his legs would carry him.

This just left Zhai Laosong and Qianzi, who could not help glowering at each other.

Zhai Laosong controlled his hatred for Qianzi and ordered, "You take the families to the east, I'll take the ones to the west!"

Qianzi folded her arms and didn't budge: "You want me to help?!"

"Qianzi, this is life and death! Everything could get wiped out! I'll pretend nothing happened between you and Maosheng today, okay?"

His tone softened a fraction.

"Okay," she said eventually.

Carrying a bundle of firewood under her arm, Pockface Zhai's wife went back indoors. Having stoked up the stove, she tiptoed back into the bedroom on her big fat feet. She sat on the edge of the *kang*, hoisted up one leg and left the other dangling over the side, then prodded her husband until he woke up. "I just saw some pretty interesting things," she whispered confidentially.

Pockface Zhai felt the cold air she brought in with her and sneezed twice. He did not open his eyes though, just wrapped the quilt tighter around his shoulders and asked listlessly: "Oh yeah? What was that?"

"Zhai Laosong just drove Maosheng out of

Qianzi's house, and that village leader of ours wasn't wearing a stitch!"

The woman gave a detailed description, deeply regretting the fact that Maosheng had actually been fully clothed, not even a button left undone.

"Uh?"

Her husband was clearly shaken. His eyes opened wide immediately.

"You should have seen Zhai Laosong's face. He was black with rage. I was quite scared! And he was carrying a gun!"

Pockface Zhai turned over and lay on his stomach, still under the quilt: "What happened then? What happened then?"

"What happened then? Er ... nothing."

"Nothing?! Didn't you say he had a gun? Was he going to shoot them?"

"No...."

Disappointed, her husband let his head drop back onto the pillow and closed his eyes.

"Why's that bell ringing?"

"I don't know...."

"Humph ... you don't know anything! Why did you bother coming in to chatter then?"

His first thought was that someone's house was on fire. A few years ago, if you didn't help when there was a fire, the very least you could expect was to get criticized at a mass meeting of the whole village. Nowadays how many people came to your aid when your house was on fire depended entirely on your popularity. Pockface Zhai couldn't be bothered to go, no matter whose house was on fire. He did not help people for nothing, and anyway there was no question of being criticized for not going to help these days. So although the sound of the bell stirred him from his early morning dreams, it did not get him out of bed.

"Strange," he mumbled with his eyes closed, "Strange that Laosong didn't teach his son-in-law and Qianzi a lesson when he caught them like that...."

His wife suddenly caught a whiff of something burning and rushed into the kitchen: she had forgotten to put water in the pot. Even the lid had nearly blackened. She rushed to pour some water in and immediately sent up billows of steam. Then she went back to her husband and continued her chatter: "And then they climbed on to Qianzi's roof...."

Pockface Zhai was given another jolt, and his eyes were immediately wide open again. He turned over in the quilt again and asked interestedly: "They fought their way up on to Qianzi's roof, eh?"

Two years ago when he had added an extension to his house, he had taken over part of Qianzi's courtyard. Qianzi had not taken it lying down, and all hell had broken loose. In the end Maosheng had intervened and protected Qianzi's rights, ordering Pockface Zhai to pay three hundred yuan and apologize to Qianzi publicly. Pockface Zhai was still brooding over this even now.

"They didn't fight their way up...."

Once again his wife's words left him disappointed.

"They went up there to have a look. Zhai Laosong said something about an ice dam up in the pass. Oh yes, and something about everyone was going to have to flee into the mountains...."

As she prattled on, Zhai Laosong rushed into the

room, ripped the quilt off Pockface Zhai and stormed: "Are you waiting to die or something? Get your children and grandchildren together and get into the mountains!" He trampled the quilt underfoot as he rushed out again.

Ice dam?

Pockface Zhai felt a stab of terror. He was, after all, a man of the world, who had heard a few things. He didn't stand there numb in the face of Zhai Laosong's warnings like that gas-bag wife of his.

He threw on his clothes, pulled on his shoes and went out into the courtyard to see, still only half convinced. He climbed up a ladder on to the roof of his house to take a look and saw immediately the towering mass of ice.

He understood what this meant.

"Oh no!"

The colour drained from his face instantly, and his legs went weak. He almost fell off the roof.

Frightened out of his wits, he scurried down the ladder, rushed back into the house and yelled: "Unbelievable! We've got to get out of here!" Then, in a series of quick, nimble movements, he removed some keys from his trouser belt, climbed on the *kang* and opened a chest, fished out a lacquered box from inside the chest, held the box close to his chest and then leapt off the *kang* again and tore out of the house.

The little lacquer box contained all his bank books and over thirty thousand yuan in ready cash. It was his life.

"Where are you going?" his wife yelled, flabbergasted.

Thinking he was on the brink of some terrible disaster, he had in his terror forgotten his responsibilities and duties as head of family. His pockmarked face flushed with shame at the realization.

"Run for your life!"

Just as he had one foot in and one foot out the door he remembered something, pulled the foot outside, back indoors and rushed into his son's room. Casting aside all propriety he ripped the quilt off his daughter-in-law and snatched the fast-asleep grandson away from her bosom. He wrapped the child up in the quilt and shouted: "You pack the colour TV and the other stuff...." He heaved the parcel of quilt and grandson up onto his shoulders and passed through the front door like a mighty, rushing wind.

The money was his life; the grandson was his lifeblood.

His wife followed him out into the courtyard and yelled after him: "You old sod! What about the children?!"

"Look at me! Do you think I can worry about them too? Let's get out of here fast ... those two are young, they can run faster ... come on!"

He had to wait for his wife a few seconds.

The old woman hesitated a moment, then ladled some water from the vat and flung it over the roaring flames in the stove. Black and white steam billowed out together through the front door and out into the courtyard.

"What the hell are you up to?"

"I've got to put out the fire. What would we do if the house caught fire?"

"Uh? You old fool!"

Pockface Zhai hopped from foot to foot in impa-

tience, and then in his anger he decided to leave behind this dawdling wife of his who remained hopeless
even in the face of death!

"For goodness sake don't forget my fox fur
coat!"

He had bought that coat for over one thousand
yuan: a beautiful silver fox fur coat.

With this yelled word of warning he rushed into the
courtyard like a stray cur.

He ran all the way to the small wooden bridge without stopping once. Hearing no one behind him, he
stopped running and stood there gasping for breath.
He was truly worn out and could not walk another
step. Never in his whole life had he had to run like
that carrying something.

The bell had stopped ringing. He felt as though the
pressing need to escape had decreased a lot in intensity.

He turned round and stared back at the village,
seeing a lot of people gathered together in a confused
mass. Some were squatting, some were standing, and
some had their hands tucked in their sleeves.

He looked up towards the mountain pass again. He
was looking at it from a different angle now, and as
he was not standing on high ground he could not see
its whole face. Only the bottom corner of it was visible
to him, the rest obscured by the mountain. The ice
dam did not seem nearly as dangerous and threatening
as it had done.

He stood there gazing dumbly at the ice dam, then
looked back towards the village again, towards his
house — the four rooms and the extension that he had
built the year before last were bathed in the beautiful
rays of the early spring sun. He could see his dog

lying by the courtyard gate. The hens had finished
laying their eggs and were now in the courtyard, broad-
casting the service they just had performed with a series
of clucks. He couldn't take the house up the mountain
with him, and he had spent an awful lot of money
buying all the furniture for it....

Although the existence of the ice dam was obviously
a fact, he began to wonder whether it really was as
horrifically dangerous as all the stories claimed, and
whether it really would be as terrible as Zhai Laosong
predicted. After all, Zhai Laosong hadn't been around
during the 19th century to experience it: he had only
had it on hearsay! And apart from him, none of the
other villagers had abandoned everything and fled the
village. Was Zhai Laosong just using the opportunity
to confuse everyone and try to set himself up as the village saviour? It was perfectly possible! Thinking this
way, he realized that his wife had been perfectly correct
to put out the fire in the stove. Because if there was a
fire and everything was burned to a cinder when it was
not washed away, Zhai Laosong would never pay
compensation. He probably couldn't even afford to....

Just as his brain terminated this laborious clanking
which passed as thought, the nerve connecting his
neckbone and collarbone reminded him to check whether his lifeblood was still in one piece. He squatted
down unhurriedly in a sort of *taiji*-type movement, gently placed the little lacquer box containing the savings
books and the ready cash down on to the planks of
the bridge, then gingerly rested the future of the clan,
still wrapped up like a spring roll in his quilt, on the
bridge too. That wooden bridge had fallen into disre-
pair long ago: the handrail shook, and there were

planks missing. Luckily the ice dam was holding the river back and there was hardly any water in the river bed, so there was no need for him to worry about his life and his lifeblood accidentally falling off the bridge and being swept away.

He unwrapped the quilt and found the three-year-old grandson's face covered in snivel and tears, his face black and his lips purple through suffocation.

"Heh, heh, poor little chap. Has your granddad hurt you? It wasn't his fault. We were running for our lives, eh!"

He mumbled away to himself and wrapped the naked lifeblood back up in his quilt again. This time he was a little kinder and more scientific in his method of wrapping, leaving the child's head poking out. This way he would be able to breathe normally, while at the same time the corner of the quilt was still protecting him from catching pneumonia.

Don't cry, little fellow. Granddad won't abandon you! No matter what happens, he'll never abandon you! You're his lifeblood, and without you, who will inherit the fortune that your granddad has schemed and worked so hard to save up?

Just thinking about it, his nose twitched. A feeling of kinship and something approaching a very touching human sympathy swamped his rich peasant mind. Standing there on the brink of a disaster that might or might not happen, he suddenly felt very heroic and admirable.

But under that pity for his fellow creatures, under that instinctive sympathy, his forever sober and practical peasant subconscious squirmed to make itself felt: he only had this one grandson! It was true that his son was still young and lusty and that his daughter-in-law seemed to go in for reproduction with great gusto, but if his grandson were to die, there was absolutely no guarantee that she would give him another grandson. It would be no use —— a complete disaster in fact —— if she gave birth to a couple of granddaughters, because nowadays, no matter how much money you were prepared to spend, the Communist Party's birth control policies never alllowed you a whole string of children. Without a grandson, even if the family fortune was flourishing more than ever, it would just get passed on to a stranger after the son died. Of course, it was true that it would probabaly still end up with one of the Zhai clan, but not all the Zhais were his children and grandchildren!

He removed his shoelaces and then tied them together. He fastened them round his waist to replace his belt, which he used to tie his irreplaceable grandson to his back. Then, hugging the little lacquer box, he got up again.

The people gathered togeher in the village had increased in number, but they were still not actually doing anything.

He wanted to get back to the village now and hear what the others thought about the ice dam, whether they thought it was really necessary to abandon everything and fly headlong into the mountains. So he walked off the bridge. However, after he had taken a few steps he stopped still, pondered a moment, and then walked back on to the bridge.

You can't take risks at a time like this, he thought to himself. You can't afford any mistakes. What would happen if you started walking and the ice dam

suddenlly collapsed? All the villagers would charge towards the bridge immediately. If you got caught in the
middle of the crowd, especially with you carrying stuff,
you'd never be the first to get to the bridge....

He marched back on to the bridge. He swayed
about a bit, and the bridge swayed with him. There
was no doubt at all that if the crowd rushed over it, it
would not be able to stand it....

He decided not to go back to the village.

He sat down on the bridge. He felt the pocket of his
jacket and was pleased to discover a packet of cigarettes, matches too.

He watched the crowd of people in the village as he
smoked.

His family had not rushed off after him after all. As
he smoked he glanced back at the ice dam and felt a
mixture of anxiety for his family and satisfaction that
he was sitting here, safe. It was a good arrangement:
he was carrying all the most important things on him,
and the rest of his family were staying back to take
care of things, so that if the whole thing turned out to
be a false alarm the family wouldn't be ridiculed by
the other villagers....

Qianzi rushed from door to door, rapping on windows
and pounding on doors. Most of the men now gathered in the middle of the village had been stirred out of
bed by her. Rubbing their eyes, yawning, mumbling
and even swearing, they had been very reluctant and
had ambled out of their homes listlessly.

Ice dam?

Run for our lives?

On such a tranquil and seemingly safe morning,

getting them to believe that they were on the brink of an awful doom was no mean feat.

What's the sodding bell ringing for when there's no fire?

During the "cultural revolution" the bell had had a sort of authority. A sort of mystique. Whenever the bell sounded, announcing "criticism meetings", distribution of labour for the day, daily readings of the works of Chairman Mao etc., everyone had gathered under the bell double quick. No one dared arrive late, because to do so betrayed ideological and emotional problems, problems of political standpoint, problems of work attitude. Work points would be deducted. In those days workpoints were the only way you could support your family and keep body and soul together. Nowadays there was no such thing as workpoints in Zhaicun Village. There had not been much land to start with, and what there was had all been contracted out to ten or so households. Now most of the Zhaicun villagers not only understood the rudiments of how to make money, they excelled at it. They would go into the county town to sell fresh vegetables, or have little deals going or household sideline production and so on and so forth. Nowadays the serious "attitude problems" of days gone by no longer existed, long since removed from the vocabulary of everyday life. The sound of the bell had not been heard for many a long year now. The battered old bell had long since lost its authority and mystique, and no one thought twice about hearing it....

The sun was still rising from the usual place.

What a beautiful morning!

In every case, what had prompted the men to con-

vene like this was a vague notion that was all that remained of their long-since hugely corroded sense of
responsibility. It was like when all the villagers met to
discuss some stupid thing or other, and the heads of
the families would go as representatives of their households. Nowadays they thought that anything not
directly affecting their families' interests was probably
something stupid and not worth discussing....

Qianzi did not call at Zhai Laogen's house.

Although she was not a vindictive person, Qianzi
had never been able to forget that time when Zhai
Laogen's wife had grabbed her by the hands and
mocked her so cruelly.

To this day, the woman had never shown any re-
morse for doing so.

The woman was calling herself the "white
witch" these days and had set up a little business in
spiritualism and divination, using all manner of ghostly
gobbledegook to swindle money out of people. Qianzi
had hoped that Maosheng would clamp down on it,
but the village head and local Party secretary had just
said, "If someone doesn't believe, they can't be
forced to believe; similarly, if someone believes, you
can't just force them not to believe. She's only
swindling a bit of money out of them, that's all. If I
had to deal with every case where people who were
quite happy to be swindled were letting themselves be
swindled, I'd never get a moment's peace."

After Guangyu died, the woman had spread the ru-
mour that Qianzi was a nine-tailed fox fairy who had
taken human form and was sent to ensnare lustful
men. In her fury, Qianzi went to find Maosheng again
and burst into tears in front of him. He laughed:

"Take no notice of her, just let her drivel on. I wish you really were a nine-tailed fox fairy in human form. If everybody believes her and keeps their distance from you so that there's just one lustful man left who's perfectly willing to be conquered by you, that won't be so bad, will it? And aren't the fox fairies in *Liaozhai** all supposed to be really beautiful and captivating? When I was young I loved that book.... I used to pray night and day that some beautiful and graceful fox fairy would come and seduce me. It looks as though the 'white witch' was right about us." Qianzi could not help laughing.

But she could not destroy her hatred for that woman. She hoped that the woman would die today.

After she had knocked on all the doors in the western half of the village, she felt as though she had finished the task that Zhai Laosong had appointed her and could go back with an easy conscience. She started running towards her home. The others might not believe that they were on the brink of a disaster, but she believed it. She didn't need to see the ice dam with her own eyes: the way that Zhai Laosong had spoken to Maosheng had made her understand that there really was a terrible danger lurking up in the mountain pass. Also, if the situation hadn't been completely desperate, would Zhai Laosong have smashed his way in through the window like that? Would Maosheng have jumped down from her roof looking so flustered and rushed off into the village like that without saying a word?

---

*Another name for *Strange Tales of Liaozhai*: a book of weird tales by Pu Songling (1640-1715).

When she went about knocking on peoples' doors, she had more or less repeated exactly what Zhai Laosong had said, adding a little colour of her own to make it sound even more urgent. She was completely amazed at the unhurried way people came out to answer their doors ... and she couldn't concentrate on just one house and ignore all the others.

She ran on and on, and then slowed down to a walk. Then she stopped walking altogether. She turned round and started running in the opposite direction. Eventually she reached Zhai Laogen's yard. His large yellow dog did not know her, and when he saw her rush into the yard looking so flustered, he barked loudly and rushed up to bite her. She was forced to beat a hasty retreat, her leg having already been bitten once. Luckily she had not changed out of her winter cotton padded trousers, and so the bite did not hurt: the dog's teeth just tore a hole in her trousers and nothing else. The dog pushed her too far, blocking the entrance to the yard, baring his fangs and barking wildly at her.

Qianzi was beside herself with anger and picked up a rock that was lying at the foot of the courtyard wall. She raised it high above her head and then hurled it in the dog's direction, scoring a direct hit on his head. The dog whimpered and slunk off to lie down by his kennel, his tail firmly between his legs. Holding the bar from the courtyard gate in her hands, she kept an eye on the dog and walked towards the window of the house. Who would have imagined that the evil animal would attack her a second time and try to bite her again? In a towering rage now, Qianzi swiped viciously at the animal with the bar. The dog rolled over on the ground, gave an even more heart-rending yowl and retreated to his kennel with one leg dragging along on the ground. With that one blow, Qianzi had evidently broken his leg.

"Which bastard's hitting my dog?" bellowed out the furious voice of Zhai Laogen.

"Me! Qianzi! Uncle Laogen, you've got to get up quick! You've got to get your whole family up! A load of ice sheets have piled up in the pass, and there's a huge ice dam which could collapse any minute."

"Is that all?"

"Yes. Didn't you hear the bell?"

"Yes. You had no right to hit my dog!"

"If I hadn't hit him, he'd have bitten me!"

Qianzi threw away the bar she was holding, turned round and hurried out of the yard.

Zhai Laogen was not an old man — not even in his fifties — and he was not deaf either. Of course he had heard the bell ringing out so urgently a moment ago. He had wanted to go and find out what was going on, but the "white witch" had clung on to him and hadn't let him get up. Using the money that the "white witch" had managed to spirit away with all her hocus-pocus, the family had bought a twenty-four-inch colour TV in town. Thanks to the times they lived in, the "white witch" had been able to start making her life more comfortable and prosperous. There was just one thing in her life that upset her: ever since she had given birth to their third daughter, Laogen had stopped showing her any affection. She would sometimes make advances to him, but he would just put on a fed-up expression and say: "What's the

point? If you have another daughter, that'll be four of
them. Just think how much we're going to have to
pay to marry them all off.'' He would often stare at
the three unmarried daughters with a worried frown,
heaving deep sighs. The years wore on, and their sex
life got worse and worse, leaving the voracious forty-
three-year-old "white witch" extremely embittered.
Then she saw an advertisement on the TV for a tonic,
whose properties, if the extravagant description was to
be believed, were nothing short of miraculous. She got
Pockface Zhai to ask a friend in town to buy ten
boxes of the stuff for Laogen, and Pockface Zhai even
had the cheek to demand twenty yuan from her for his
services. Zhai Laogen had already got through two
boxes of the stuff, but he remained the same old
unstirrable Laogen. When she asked him what he
thought of the medicine, he remarked that it was very
sweet, like syrup. Last night the "white witch" had
forced him to up the dosage. After taking it he said
that he could feel the power of the medicine. "How do
you feel?'' she asked. "Sleepy,'' he replied, and des-
pite all her attempts to excite him, he was soon asleep
and snoring thunderously....

"Don't get up! Don't listen to the little vixen! If
it's really as dangerous as she makes out, then how
come everything's so quiet? There would be a real
racket if what she said was true, and she would have
saved herself long ago. She wouldn't be so kind as to
come and tell us about it. I bet they're trying to get
some volunteers to go up and work in the pass or
dredge the river or something....''

She clung on to him.

"I'm going to get up and see what kind of state

the dog's in."

"He's not yelping!"

"Well I've still got to get up. We can't just laze in bed all day. What sort of example is that to the girls?"

"You're not getting up! Don't you want a son?"
Silence.

"You've given up, eh? Well, I haven't. Don't give up.... Bet if I get pregnant it'll be a son! I've worked it out, today's the best time to try...."

In the face of her nagging, Laogen just had to do as she wanted.

Qianzi walked out of their courtyard and then turned back to look. Seeing that the door had not opened, she walked back and stood in front of the window.

"Uncle Laogen!"

Inside all was perfectly still. Zhai Laogen did not utter a word of reply.

"Uncle Laogen! For goodness sake get up! I'm telling the truth ... I wouldn't be up this early just to play a trick on you! If you don't get up I'll smash your window!"

Still no sound from the room.

Qianzi picked up the bar again and, using the Zhai Laosong's method, she gave the glass an almighty crack, smashing Zhai Laogen's window to smithereens. As she smashed, she felt that her duty was at last fully accomplished. She also felt as though she had got her revenge in public over her adversary, and a carefree feeling overtook her. When she had finished, she tossed the bar into the room too....

"Qianzi you little bitch! You think I don't know about what you get up to? You're not getting away with this. I'm going to fix it so there's no one in this village who doesn't spit in your face...." As she ran out of the courtyard she heard Zhai Laogen's wife hurl a torrent of abuse at her.

On her way, she ran into Maosheng.

"What are you still doing here?" he asked, angry at seeing her. "Do you think it's all some sort of big game? Don't you even believe me?"

"I believe you, I believe you," she explained. "Your old man told me to go and wake everybody on this side of the village. He looked so evil that I didn't dare refuse."

"Have you woken them all?"

"Yes."

"Then how come there's hardly anyone out?"

"They won't believe me! The worst was Zhai Laogen.... I smashed in his window and that wife of his swore her head off at me!"

"You'd better get out of here then. Your job's finished!"

"How come I didn't hear you making your broadcast?"

"Ha! We haven't used that thing for ages.... How was I to know it was broken? I tinkered with it for ages, but I couldn't get it mended. Now listen, you've got to get out of here!"

"What about you? How come you're not off? Are you waiting to die like the rest of them?"

"Don't bother about me! I'm the village head and the local Party secretary, and I've been getting my hundred yuan a year worry money. If I die now I'm just getting what I deserve...."

Without saying another word, Maosheng rushed off

in the direction of the building where the old bell hung.

Zhai Laosong's son Jinsuo was ringing the bell.

"Oy, you lot, I wasn't ringing the bell to gather you all in one place so you could wait to be killed together! What are you doing hanging around?"

The young boy yelled at the villagers at the top of his voice, carrying out his selfless task conscientiously.

"We're waiting for your dad!" someone yelled back.

"What are you waiting for him for? There's no need! Run for your lives! I know my dad, and he won't run off before you do...."

"Do you think that we're going to take our families and troop up the mountain like a flock of sheep just because of what some kid says? What a joke! I've never heard of that happening in Zhaicun Village before!"

"Aiya, aiya! What's there to understand? If you don't believe me, I'll go first!"

"Go on then, sonny! Go on then!"

The men roared with laughter.

The youth stared dumbly at the crowd, not knowing what to do.

He had felt the terror rising in him for a while already.

But he did not run.

He did not want to abandon his father.

Someone asked: "Have you actually seen this ice dam, Jinsuo? How high is it?"

"Of course I've seen it! It was me who showed it to Dad, honest!"

Someone climbed up the tree.

"I see it, I see it! It's like a huge city wall!"

"Come down, I want to take a look!"

As one came down, another went up.

"Wow! What a sight! It's all silvery and dazzling.... It really does look like a city wall!"

Someone down below suddenly yelled up: "Hey! Whose house is that on fire?"

The man up the tree stopped looking at the ice dam and looked towards the village instead: "It's Zhai Laosong's house! Zhai Laosong's house is on fire!"

The moment he heard this, Jinsuo took off as fast as his legs would carry him, back towards his home. Before he had got very far, however, Zhai Laosong stopped him: "Hey! Where do you think you're going?"

"Dad, our house is on fire!"

"I know. I set it on fire."

"......"

Jinsuo stared at his father as if he didn't recognize him.

"If I hadn't ... we obviously couldn't keep it any way." Zhai Laosong spoke especially calmly as he stared at the leaping flames. He ruffled his son's hair and said: "Listen, I want you to escape to the mountains now. Don't stop on the way. Run up to the top in one go!"

"Dad, I'm staying with you. I'm not going anywhere. If I live, we both live; if I die, I die together with you...."

"Run, you stupid bastard, or I'll belt you one!"

His son stood there, obstinately refusing to budge.

"Run!"

Zhai Laosong gave his son a vicious whack on the bum with the butt of his rifle.

Jinsuo was knocked to the ground. He got up and cried silently. He stared at his father, his eyes full of tears, and then ran away.

"Don't you dare stop! Don't turn back! If you stop I'll shoot you!"

His son tore out of the village, not looking back even once.

That morning, standing in that village that had lost all sense of authority, that had even lost all sense of prestige and trust, all sense of mutual tolerance, all sense of togetherness and all sense of responsibility, Zhai Laosong had at long last realized how difficult it would be for him, a man who wasn't respected any more, to get over a thousand people together in such a short space of time.

He would use fire to warn the people.

Fire started in another part of the village.

It was village leader Maosheng's house.

Maosheng had understood too and used the same means to warn the people.

Before lighting the fire he remembered to open all the rabbit hutches....

As he watched all those overfed fat rabbits, a feeling of sadness overtook him: when his wife returned, the house would no longer exist. If he did not exist either, how would she manage? The loss of over seven thousand rabbits would leave her ten thousand yuan out of pocket!

He finally realized that the fact that they had lived together so many years and he had never really loved her was actually a sin....

Zhai Laosong hurried to the area where the men were gathered together and said: "Have you seen?

I've set my house on fire! Why have I done that? Because it doesn't matter whether I set it on fire or not ... it'll still be wiped off the face of the earth either way. When that ice dam goes, nothing in this village will be left!''

Some looked at the fire, others looked towards the pass, others listened to him petrified, and still others looked at each other in dismay....

Maosheng walked up and added: "I've set my house on fire too. You elected me village leader, and in that position I order you to escape into the mountains. If you hurry, you stand a good chance. If you go slowly, don't blame anyone for what happens! That's all!''

Just as his voice trailed off, the mountain gave a rumble....

Everyone looked up towards the pass.

They saw a huge block of ice carried over by the river water. In a twinkling, the river bed was full again. The little wooden bridge was smashed by the block of ice, its skeleton carried away by the river....

Zhai Laosong and Maosheng did not need to utter another word: the crowd fled in all directions.

"Party members stay where you are!" roared Zhai Laosong, firing a shot into the air. "Laogen, you're a Party member!''

"Not any more! I resign!''

Everyone disappeared. Apart from the son-in-law who was still standing next to him and hadn't moved, not a single other Party member was to be seen.

But instead of running out of the village, everyone was running back to their homes. Once they got home, they shouted at the tops of their voices, barred the courtyard gates, shut all the doors, blocked up the windows, climbed up trees or clambered on to their roofs ... getting them to abandon all their riches and flee empty-handed to the mountain was going to prove even more difficult.

The well-off families all had colour TVs, tape recorders and nice clothes in their homes ... all the things that they had accumulated over the years that represented wealth.

It was as though they wanted to live or die with their wealth. As though they believed that the steps they were taking could somehow avert the disaster.

However, the ice dam had only shed a tiny corner. Before long, the floe-bearing river was shallow again, flowing away rapidly into the distance. Gradually the river bed became dry again, leaving behind countless huge blocks of ice, like beached silver rafts. Apart from the little smashed bridge there was not much damage.

Rejoicing broke out throughout the village. The villagers were convinced that the danger had already passed, and they congratulated themselves on the fact that they and their possessions were all safe and sound.

Zhai Laosong and Zhai Maosheng's houses were now just smouldering ruins, filling the air with dark smoke. The whole village was full of the lung-searing smoke.

"God have mercy! God have mercy!"

Zhai Laosong flopped down on his knees in the middle of the village and kowtowed in the direction of the mountain again and again, praying devoutly on the villagers' behalf: "Mountain gods, river gods, earth gods ... save this village I beseech you! Help me now and after I die I'll become a dog or a horse and work for you!"

"Dad, get up! This is no time to beg the gods!"

This son-in-law, who had never lightly called him "dad" in his whole life, was giving him a chance to be close to him.

"Who else should I beg, eh?"

Zhai Laosong was seething with anger, as though his son-in-law had just insulted him. He got up, pulled his double-barrelled shotgun down from his shoulder, stuffed two bullets into the bore and gritted his teeth: "Fire! We've got to set their houses on fire! You light the fires and I'll help you! We'll drive them out of the village and up the mountain even if we have to whip them and beat them!"

"That's what I was thinking too!"

The son-in-law approved.

Fire!

Fire!

Fire....

Conflagrations burst out all around the village.

Villagers who had previously been unwilling to leave their homes were driven out by the fire. Women were crying, children screaming, men swearing, old people trembling in a scene of total confusion.

The sky wasn't so sunny any more.

The dawn wasn't so tranquil.

"Zhai Maosheng, you little son-of-a-bitch!"

"You whoring widow-snatcher, I'm going to take you to court!"

"We've had it out with you, Laosong, you old bastard!"

But Zhai Laosong had a gun in his hands, and the bloodthirsty and evil expression on his face made it perfectly clear that he wasn't at all worried about the legal repercussions of killing someone, and no one dared fight him.

No matter how the villagers cursed them, father-and son-in-law carried on turning a deaf ear and did not utter a word in reply. One of them brandishing a rifle and the other with a blazing torch in each hand, they ran round the village, spreading fire wherever they went. They spared no one....

As Qianzi got to the river bank and was about to cross the blocks of ice to the other side, she suddenly noticed Pockface Zhai lying on one of the blocks, his face turned upwards and his two dead eyes staring at the sun. She screamed with fright. He was still clasping the little lacquer box tightly to his chest, and his grandson was squashed underneath him. His legs were clamped between two blocks of ice. She plucked up all the courage she could muster and approached him. She squatted down beside him and passed her hand before his mouth and nose but felt no breath. On a block of ice a couple of yards away lay his severed arm, still in its sleeve, sheered off by the ice. His grandson's hair poked out from behind his shoulder.

Qianzi quickly loosened his belt and with a gargantuan effort managed to raise him up. She loosened her grip on him and gave him a shove, so that he fell face first and crashed on to the pebbles. She felt something splatter over her whole face but couldn't be bothered to wipe it off. She picked up the quilt-wrapped child and marvelled at how empty the quilt felt. She opened it to take a look and gave a screech of horror, covering her face and dropping to the ice, her whole body shaking with uncontrollable sobs.

The quilt was just filled with gore.

Only the child's head remained intact....

Zhaicun Village was a sea of flame.

The first group of villagers was driven like a herd of cattle by the gun-wielding Zhai Laosong, yelling his head off.

The moment she saw them, Qianzi stopped crying. She prized open Pockface Zhai's hands to grab the lacquer box. Then she jumped up and ran to meet them, wanting to help the women with children. She kept slipping and stumbling over the blocks of ice that were in her way.

The villagers were all being driven by Zhai Laosong and Zhai Maosheng. The men were leading cows, horses, donkeys and mules; the women were carrying things of all shapes and sizes. It had proved impossible to get them to abandon everything. The children stumbled and tripped as they were pulled along, and dogs threaded in and out of the crowd looking for their masters....

The village, which was now just a burning lake, never saw a man again. Chickens, ducks and geese were being roasted and flappping around desperately, not knowing where to hide. Some cats had climbed a large tree and were yowling in terror.

Zhai Laosong was still grimly holding on to his hunting rifle as he stood in the middle of the crossroads, his legs planted firmly apart. His badger fur hat had long since disappeared, goodness knows where, and his face was covered in spit, a present from some of the women.

"Is there anyone left who hasn't escaped?" he roared.

Suddenly a pig appeared out of nowhere and charged up to him, winking. It stopped in front of him and stood there, its blinking pig eyes staring at him as though studying him. Then it ran away again, oinking as it went.

When you do a thing you should do it properly. An uncontrollable sense of mission spurred him on and urged him to go through the village again and help the people who were still there to escape.

In a little shack that Zhai Laogen used as a storeroom, he discovered Zhai Laogen's eighty-nine-year-old mother sitting crosslegged on a *kang* covered with a dirty blanket; her eyes were shut, the palms of her hands together in prayer, and she was muttering incantations.

Her son, her daughter-in-law, and her grandchildren had had no time to think of her in their panic to get out. They had abandoned her. Luckily the little shack was close to the gate and not attached to the main part of the house — it was actually a good twenty metres away — so the fire in the house had not spread to the shack. Otherwise she would have been ashes by now.

Cats, chickens, ducks and geese, as well as the dog whose leg had been broken by Qianzi, were spread over the *kang* and on the floor, crowding the little shack.

"Third grandmother!"

This was the respectful title that Zhai Laosong owed her according to family rank.

The old woman opened her eyes unhurriedly, gave him an indifferent look, then shut her eyes and started her incantations again.

"Third grandmother, everyone in the village has left. I'll carry you out!"

He leapt on to the *kang* and bent over to pick the old woman up.

She stopped her incantations: "Don't touch me." Her voice was very quiet, but Zhai Laosong could hear the severity of the tone.

"Third grandmother, I'm your junior.... It's my duty to carry you out. Come on, let me pick you up...."

As he spoke he tried to force her.

The old woman's scrawny hands bunched up into little fists and they pounded against his back like drumsticks. Next she pinched his face, pinched his neck and bit his ears.

"Don't bite my ears!"

There was no way he could carry her like this.

"My son shows me no respect, my daughter-in-law mistreats me, my grandchildren don't even think I'm human.... I'm so old, I should have died long ago: what's the point in running off? Today's my big chance...."

Zhai Laosong's face fell.

"Well ... is there anything I can do for you, third grandmother?"

Her eyes opened and stared at him: "Help me open that chest down there on the floor. There are some funeral clothes in there that I made myself years ago. You can help your third grandmother put them on...."

Hearing this, Zhai Laosong jumped on to the floor and opened the chest. He pulled out a pair of trousers and a gown made of old blue cloth from the bottom of the chest; they had been pressed flat like card and starched and dyed. Zhai Laosong jumped back on to the *kang* and slowly clothed the old woman in the twenty-year-old outfit.

"Could . . . could you draw the curtain for me too? I don't want to see anything."

In spite of himself, his mind raced back to his childhood and the days when he used to come regularly to steal and eat raw eggs from third grandmother's chicken coop. One time she had caught him, but instead of ranting at him or dragging him off to report him to his parents, she had just told him that if he ate raw eggs he would get an upset stomach, and that in the future, if he was feeling hungry he should come and tell her, and she would boil some eggs for him....

"Third grandmother, is there anything else you want me to do?"

She shook her head imperceptibly and her eyes remained shut tight.

"Don't worry, third grandmother, when the anniversary of your death comes round I'll burn paper for you...."

She nodded slightly to show that she heard him and believed him.

"Third grandmother...."

He knelt down and kowtowed to the old woman three times, his head knocking on the floor each time.

The chickens, ducks, geese, cat and dog all looked at him with an almost human expression of tranquillity in their eyes.

He stood up slowly, wiped the corner of his eyes, and strode out with his head hung low....

The village leader had not set fire to the community

hall. This was because there was nothing of value there that anyone would risk death to protect.

Its door was left wide open, the megaphone scattered in pieces in the threshold.

When Zhai Laosong went in, the phone was ringing.

He hesitated a moment, then strode past it.

At a time like this, when death could come any moment, he didn't feel like answering it.

But the increasingly urgent ringing pursued him like the cries of a person begging for attention.

Something stopped him in his tracks. Hesitating no longer, he ran back to the hall and picked up the receiver.

"Hello! Is that the Zhai community hall?"

"Yes. Who are you?"

"The county Party committee. Have you discovered the ice dam yet?"

"Ages ago. The villagers are all up in the mountains now."

"Good! That ice dam's got to be blown up immediately! The river's burst its banks higher up, three villages are flooded, and there are over a hundred people stranded on the roofs of their houses. Do you understand?"

"...."

"Do you understand?!"

"Yes."

"Who are you?"

"Zhai Laosong."

"Listen here, Zhai Laosong, I'm writing down your name! If you delay the rescue, it's you I'm coming after!"

He hung up.

Zhai Laosong slowly put the receiver back in its cradle.

Knowing at last that he was not going to be able to leave the village, he felt a horror of loneliness in the face of death. It was greater than his terror of the ice dam.

Who was that who had just rung? The county head? The secretary of the county Party committee? Or just some functionary? Whoever it was, he was representing the county Party committee. It was an order and had to be obeyed whether he liked it or not. It was as though the order was for Zhai Laosong himself. He knew the old county head and the old secretary of the county Party committee. And they knew him. They would not have been so unfamiliar with his name and would not have spoken to him in such a severe tone of voice. But the county officials had already changed three times, and there were only a very few left now that he knew. Ones who knew him were very thin on the ground too.

But it was clear that he had received an order.

"Shit! It's me that'll get blamed!"

He smashed the telephone to bits with the butt of his rifle.

Zhai Laosong strode out of the village towards a disused grain mill to the north. There, under a millstone covered with wild grass a metre or so high, lay enough gunpowder to blow up the ice dam, a fuse just over a metre long, and several detonators. This was the sum total of public property left from the village quarry in the years when he had been village leader. Later, when they had implemented the contracting policy and public property had been distributed, he had hidden it there for his own personal use. The bullets that he used when he went hunting he made for himself using that gunpowder. He used to take the detonators with him when he went far upstream to dynamite fish, and he still had a few left.

In the thirty years that he had served the Zhaicun villagers, this had been his one and only act of corruption, and it was known to no one else but himself.

The leg that Zhai Laosong had injured up by the ice dam started really hurting. He was almost an old man after all. In all the confusion a few moments ago he had not felt it, but now the pain was making it hard for him to run.

What do you want to run for anyway?

He slackened his pace, thinking to himself as he walked: When you took the task of blowing up the ice dam from that county guy, you were telling him you were willing to die! You don't think you'll be able to blow it up and live, do you? Zhai Laosong, Zhai Laosong, you silly old fool ... what did you have to go and answer that telephone call for? And what are you doing now, running like mad? Are you worried you won't die soon enough?

So he stopped running, shouldered his rifle, and began to walk at a leisurely pace. He still could not bring himself to throw his rifle away, thinking it might come in useful between now and when he died.

Suddenly he gritted his teeth and ran on through the pain. He thought of the villages upstream that had been submerged and all those people perched on their roofs in the middle of a vast sea, hoping to be saved.

Thanks to that county official, all their lives have been entrusted to me, he thought. I'd better run.

All around him was a sea of flames. Some houses had already totally collapsed in the fire, their beams all burnt. There was no trace of any living thing. The smoke was thick, making him cough incessantly and his eyes and nose stream.

The villagers must all be in some safe place on the upper slopes of the mountain by now, mustn't they?

He felt wronged. He felt lonely and suffocated. He felt a sense of terrible injustice.

But he kept gritting his teeth and ignoring the pain in his leg as best he could, urging himself on towards the mill, faster and faster. Something tripped him up. He picked himself up and ran on....

The people who had gone up the mountain and could now see the full menace of the deadly ice dam from their vantage point no longer cursed Zhai Laosong and Zhai Maosheng. They now just kept looking at the fire in the village and regretting their terrible loss, worrying about the total destitution that would be theirs.

The day ripped through the dawn's tinfoil-coloured afterbirth, and before all the mist had completely dispersed, it aborted the last traces of rose-coloured sky. The rising sun leapt up gracefully from the "lake" in the gorge behind the ice dam and then rose in its entirety, stately and splendid. The "lake" was covered with blocks of ice, sparkling with a silver light in the brilliant sunshine. In the still swelling river water, the blocks of ice crushed against each other and piled up on top of each other, forming little ice mountains. It was a sight of unparalleled beauty that the Zhaicun villagers had never before witnessed.

The towering ice dam grew more and more magnificent. The danger of this brittle and false structure multiplied quietly. Ten times over. A hundred times over.

"Who's that? Who's that still running around the village?!"

"It's Qianzi, isn't it?"

"She must be mad! Quick, yell to her!"

Some of the men and women started to yell.

"Qianzi!"

"Qianzi! Come back here quick!"

"Qianzi! The ice dam's about to go!"

Although Qianzi heard the yells she still crossed the river and carried on running as fast as she could towards the village.

As she ran she yelled: "Maosheng! Maosheng!"

But Maosheng was in the village looking for Zhai Laosong.

"Dad! Where are you, dad?"

Qianzi followed the yells and found Maosheng. Out of breath, she panted, "Maosheng! I came back to look for you. Everyone's up the mountain. What are you doing wandering around here? Let's get out of here!"

"You silly bitch! Who asked you to come looking for me?"

He wanted to beat her up.

Seeing her about to burst into tears, he gestured towards the mountain and shouted: "Don't cry! And stop playing the tragic heroine who's going to die with her lover. Leave! Now!"

"Who said anythig about dying with you? I was just worried that you....."

"All right, all right, don't say it!" he cut her off, "Come with me and look for Dad then. When we find him we can all escape!''

"Dad! Dad!''

"Uncle Laosong! Uncle Laosong!''

They joined forces to yell.

"Stop shouting! I'm not dead!''

Zhai Laosong suddenly appeared behind them. He was wearing his vest and sleeveless jacket on top, and his padded jacket was in his hands, wrapped around something or other. The gun was still on his shoulder.

"Dad, come with us ... everyone's saved!''

"You two go, I'm not leaving for the mountain!''

"But dad, you....''

Zhai Laosong related the order from the county to the astonished Maosheng and Qianzi.

Zhai Laosong caught sight of his son-in-law and Qianzi holding hands and his brows knotted.

Maosheng did not notice, however, and volunteered: "You and Qianzi leave quickly! I'll go and blow up the ice dam!''

"I was given the order, and I don't need you showing off!'' Zhai Laosong replied angrily, "You leave! Qianzi will stay here with me to blow up the ice dam!''

Qianzi and Maosheng stared at each other and then stared at Zhai Laosong's emotionless face, as though they could not immediately fully understand what he had just said.

"Let go of her hand and get out of here!''

Zhai Laosong's cold eyes were now fixed on just his son-in-law, as though Qianzi, who was standing in front of him too, simply didn't exist. As though he didn't see her. His tone was brutal.

Maosheng let go of Qianzi's hand at once and said

slowly: "That isn't fair, dad. How can you do it? Let Qianzi go. You and I'll do the job!"

"Shut up! Get out of here! I told you to get out of here!"

A plan had formed in Zhai Laosong's mind. He didn't think he was being selfish in the least, much less vicious. What father doesn't try to help his own daughter out when he can? Believing himself to be completely in the right, he gripped Qianzi's wrist tightly and started dragging her away.

"Dad! You can't do this!"

Maosheng streched out his arms to bar the way.

He let go of Qianzi.

Qianzi had just reached Maosheng's side when Zhai Laosong took down his double-barrelled hunting rifle, raised it to his shoulder and pressed it straight in Qianzi's chest, his finger on the trigger.

"If you don't do as I say, I'll kill you."

The bleak tone in which he spoke made him sound completely heartless.

Qianzi's beautiful eyes fixed on the barrel of the gun as Zhai Laosong forced her, terror-stricken, to retreat step by step.

"Dad!" Maosheng followed behind them, begging tearfully, "If you're set on killing one of us two to-day, I'll die with you! Don't force Qianzi!"

"You're the village leader! The village will still need you after today! If Qianzi dies, it'll be to her glory!"

Zhai Laosong spat out the words, not even glancing at his son-in-law.

"Dad!"

"If you take another step, I'll fire!" he roared.

He looked so tyrannical that Zhai Maosheng was

frozen to the spot.

"Uncle Laosong! You took the job. It's got nothing to do with me! I'm not doing it! I'm not going to blow up the ice dam!"

Qianzi's tears streamed down her face, but as the black muzzle of the gun was still pressed tightly against her chest she had to keep retreating towards the pass, towards the ice dam.

"Dad!"

Zhai Laosong turned around abruptly —— Bang! A bullet whizzed past Maosheng, just missing him.

"That was just a warning! The second bullet's for her! I'm going to count to three, and if you're not running towards the mountain, she won't even make it as far as the pass!"

"Qianzi, run!"

Qianzi realized that she had to run, but Zhai Laosong's rifle had already turned back and was pointing at her chest again, almost touching it.

Zhai Laosong leant to one side. Using the rifle to force Qianzi to keep on walking and turning his head back to watch Maosheng at the same time, he yelled: "One! ... Two!...."

Maosheng started running.

"Qianzi! Qianzi ... you shouldn't have come back for me! Zhai Laosong, you scumbag, becoming your son-in-law was the worst thing that ever happened to me!"

As he ran, he kept looking back, yelling, swearing.

Qianzi finally understood what Zhai Laosong's game was, and having understood, she stopped crying. She stopped being afraid of dying. She stopped trying to make him pity her.

A noble self-respect gave her strength.

She looked at Zhai Laosong mockingly and gave a cold laugh: "Put the gun down. You don't need to force me. I'll die with you. Because we will die, won't we? If you're not scared, neither am I! I deserve to die, and when I do, it'll be one less worry for your daughter, won't it?"

In the face of her strength and with his real motive laid bare, Zhai Laosong felt ashamed.

The gun lowered.

But Qianzi did not run off.

"I'll carry the explosives," she said, "You rest!" She streched out her hands to receive the explosives.

In spite of himself, Zhai Laosong handed over the padded jacket which contained the explosives. His hands were really feeling tired.

As he handed them over, something dropped out from the front of Qianzi's jacket: three bundles of money.

The three thousand yuan that Qianzi had told Maosheng she hadn't had time to put into her savings account.

The two of them stared dumbly at the money.

Qianzi was the first to speak: "Quick, let's go!" She left the money where it was and strode off in front.

Zhai Laosong did not move. He looked from Qianzi to the money on the ground. His heart, corroded with viciousness a moment before, softened instantly in a fit of kindness. It was as though he could see into Qianzi's heart. He understood how much this young widow loved life, loved living. She was only twenty-seven years old! How could she be compared with an old stick like him, who had no youth left and no passionate desire for life? Zhai Laosong, Zhai Laosong, you're in the wrong.... You've sinned!

"Stop!"

She stopped and turned back with a surprised look on her face.

"I can blow up the ice dam on my own. You ... you can go after Maosheng! I'll wait until you two are up the mountain before I light the fuse...."

Qianzi stood there hesitantly, as though she could not quite believe him.

"Put the explosives down!"

Qianzi put them down obediently.

"What are you waiting for? Run!"

Qianzi kept her eyes fixed on him as she walked, in case he tried to shoot her in the back.

"I'm not tricking you. Run!"

Qianzi turned and started running after Maosheng.

"Wait!"

Qianzi stopped again.

"Catch!"

Zhai Laosong bent over, picked up the bundles of money and threw them over to her, one by one.

After Qianzi had caught them all, Zhai Laosong said: "And tell Maosheng he'd better not leave my Xiumei! And he'd better not bully her! And you two aren't allowed to keep seeing each other!"

He picked up the explosives, threw down the gun, and strode off....

The villagers up the mountain could see three people still in the danger zone, but had no way of telling what was going on between them, much less hear what

they were yelling at each other. They were amazed to
see Zhai Laosong heading for the ice dam. They
couldn't guess what he was up to.

"Dad! Dad! Dad!"

Zhai Laosong couldn't hear his son's yells either.

He gave one last longing look back at the people on
the mountain, realizing that he didn't really hate them
anywhere near as much as he had thought. Not even
those he had previously thought of as scum. He still
bore their safety in mind.

He saw his son. His son was standing alone on a
large black rock and kept waving to him. He stood
still a moment and waved back.

His eyes were moist.

He thought to himself: Jinsuo, I don't want to die,
but it's my fate! Why did I have to answer that telephone?

Carrying the little lacquer box that Qianzi had given
her, Pockface Zhai's widow bewailed her husband's
cruel death.

But her son and daughter-in-law were weeping bitterly over the loss of their son, and their cries were pep-
pered with curses for Pockface Zhai.

After a while, the son stopped crying and went up to
his mother: "Mum, give me the lacquer box! I get
nervous seeing you holding it. What would happen
if...."

Sitting down on the mountain slope, she started to
curse: "Your father's dead and you're trying to
snatch my money box?! I bet it's that little bitch of a
wife of yours who put you up to it! Well I'm not
dead yet, so you can forget it!"

Lynx-like, the daughter-in-law rushed over and

clawed at her. Seeing her turn so nasty, Pockface Zhai's widow jumped to her feet and wove her way through the crowd, yelling: "She's trying to kill me! Help!"

Some of the men restrained the daughter-in-law, who fought them tooth and nail, even biting some people's hands. One of the men backhanded her across the face, and she calmed down and started crying over her dead son again....

Zhai Laogen's wife was reading the palms of a large group of women who surrounded her. Unbelievably, she had the gall to say: "This disaster was predestined! The name Zhai is inauspicious, and its bad luck rubbed off on to the village when we called it Zhaicun Village. 'Zhai' sounds the same as 'zai'* when you say it fast. We've been saying the word everyday.... No wonder we invoked a disaster. Actually, I predicted this disaster eight days ago!"

"Shut your stinking mouth! If you knew about it eight days ago, why didn't you say anything about it earlier?" Zhai Laogen gestured at her furiously. Looking at the flames and smoke dancing throughout the village, he felt a sudden pang of pity for the mother he had abandoned, secretly afraid that he would pay the reckoning for this sin when he reached the nether world. A part of him wanted to rush down the mountain to save her, but he didn't dare take the risk. He felt a hundred insects gnawing at his heart.

"That's what I meant. But the Gods didn't allow me to say it. You know bugger all, so why don't you just get lost, eh? Listen, I can tell you all how much

---

*Zai is Chinese for "disaster".

wealth you'll get back after the disaster! Fifty fen for a rough estimate, one yuan for a more accurate one! You've got no cash on you? Right, wait a minute then, I'll get my daughter to write up an account. Ready cash gets priority! Oh dear, your palm doesn't look too hopeful!''

She wasn't worried —— if the skies fell, she would find others to prop them up for her. Everyone was in the same penniless plight. Before they had made their escape, she had got her daughters to carry out all the valuables. Now she could grab a bit of ready cash too....

Zhai Laogen didn't believe in his wife's trickery. Giving a snort of disgust, he left in search of some peace and quiet....

Ice dam, ice dam, when we were terrified you were going to collapse, you looked as if you would do so at any moment. When we wanted you to collapse, why didn't you? Why did you have to wait for me to come right up to you to blow you up? Out of the thousand villagers, why were you only interested in killing me, Zhai Laosong?

Thinking such thoughts, Zhai Laosong had reached the bottom of the ice dam and was no longer visible to the people on the mountainside. He could no longer see them either. The overhanging crest of the ice dam, like the brim of a hat, blocked the sky from his view. The coldness around the bottom of the ice dam assailed him, and he couldn't help shivering. He wanted to see the sun again but couldn't. Outside the huge shadow of the ice dam, however, the sun was still shining very bright.

Come on, Laosong, you mustn't dawdle, he said to

himself. There's nothing to be gained by dawdling. You can't run away from fate....

Just as Zhai Laosong put down the explosives, a block of ice toppled over the lip of the ice dam and buried him under a pile of smashed ice, taking him unawares. The smashed ice formed a sort of crystal tomb for him.

Zhai Maosheng and Qianzi, who had just run to the foot of the mountain, saw the whole thing clearly.

They both stopped running.

Maosheng said, "He's finished."

Qianzi said, "How horrible."

"Qianzi, it's my turn now. If he hadn't told me about the telephone call and I knew nothing about it, it would be forgivable if I didn't go now. But he did tell me. I do know. I'm village leader. I'm a Party member.... You take care of yourself from now on. I've got to go!"

Without waiting for her to answer, he sped off towards the dam. Without stopping, he ran all the way to the place where Zhai Laosong was buried. Not waiting to catch his breath back, he started digging his way through the blocks of ice, big and small, with his bare hands. From afar the pile of ice looked like a burial mound; only when you got close to it could you see that it was actually ten times bigger than any burial mound. The more desperately he tried to dig up the explosives quickly, the more he felt frustrated, unable to channel his body's energy through his hands.

Eventually, when his fingers were all bloody and his head was covered in sweat, he dug the explosives out. Luckily, the gunpowder, fuse and detonators were all wrapped up in the cotton-padded jacket and were bone

dry. Maosheng had worked in a quarry before in charge of explosives, so he worked quickly and smoothly.

He got the matches out of Zhai Laosong's jacket,
but because he had been moving all that ice, his hands
were dripping and he accidentally soaked the striking
surface of the matchbox. He broke several matches but
could not get any of them to light. Then, when one
did light, the wind blew it out again. Up in the pass,
the wind was really strong. As all around was ice,
nothing was actually moving, but you could hear the
wind whistle.

"Hello...."

He looked up in surprise and saw Qianzi squatting
in front of him.

"Qianzi, you can't love anyone that much! I'm
not worth dying with...."

"I didn't come just to die with you. Anyway,
Uncle Laosong told both of us, not just you. When I
saw you couldn't light the explosives I had to come
back. You strike the match, I'll shelter you...."

Maosheng stood there staring at this woman whom
he loved so much but who wasn't fated to be his, and
he didn't know what to do.

Qianzi said nothing, just took off her padded jacket.
Having removed this, she took off her cotton jumper
leaving only her flowery cloth blouse and the maroon
coloured bra inside.

"What are you doing?"

"I was in such a hurry to run to you, I forgot to
leave my money somewhere where the water wouldn't
reach it...."

She wrapped the three bundles of money tightly up
in the jumper and then, copying Zhai Laosong's method

of wrapping up the explosives, she put the jumper in the middle of her padded jacket and used the sleeves of the jacket to tie it all up. Then she looked at him and asked: "If I do this do you think someone will find it?"

"Yes," he replied softly, thinking only of soothing her for all the pains she had taken.

"I hope so," she laughed softly. "It'll be better than the flood washing it away and no one being able to use it! That's what I saved through eating frugally and never wearing nice clothes. Strike the match! Go on! I'll shelter you...."

She came even closer.

His hands were shaking violently and he snapped some more matches.

"Do you want me to do it?"

"No, no, I'm fine."

At long last a match caught.

She sheltered the flame with both hands.

He lit the fuse.

The fuse was just over a metre long. It spluttered along, giving off sparks.

They watched the fuse getting shorter and shorter.

"There's no point running now anyway," he mumbled to himself.

"I know.... What will it feel like?"

"You won't feel a thing...."

"I'm cold."

He hugged her to him tightly.

"Shut your eyes, that way you won't be scared."

She had shut her eyes ages ago.

He was about to shut his eyes too, but he didn't have the time.

They heard nothing.

The two tightly-clasped bodies were blown to smithereens in an instant, pieces of flesh flying skywards and mixing with the shards of crystal filling the sky. Then they splattered everywhere in a roaring end-of-the century tidal wave....

Only their souls, still clinging on to life, knew their exemption from the horror of death.

Terrified, they took flight over the billowing waves of ice, then in a moment vanished.

Zhaicun Village was wiped off the face of the earth.

The county head came to inspect the area where Zhaicun Village had once been.

There were no scenes of destruction to be seen. There was just nothing. Nothing to be seen at all.

The topography of the area had changed drastically. It looked like rotting skin.

The head of the county cried and gave the Zhaicun villagers many words of consolation, encouraging them to rebuild their homes. Then he asked: "Is there someone called Zhai Laosong living here?"

They all replied that there was.

"Bring him to me quick."

"He's dead!"

"Dead?"

"He died blowing up the ice dam."

The head of the county fell silent, thinking to himself: I only ordered him to blow up the ice dam. I didn't order him to die! I didn't have time to think about whether he'd live or die....

With a heavy heart, he finally spoke up again: "Zhai Laosong died for a good cause. You should make a monument to him to serve as a shining example to later generations of Zhais!''

Zhai Laogen spoke up: ''But we're absolutely destitute. If a monument's to go up, it'll have to be the county that pays for it!''

The head of the county replied: ''The county won't abandon you all. You can be sure of that! We'll allocate emergency funds to everyone. As for the money for the monument, we'll be more than happy to pay.''

Zhai Laogen continued: ''Two others died, and one of them was village head. Will you be setting up monuments for them too?''

''It depends on how they died,'' sighed the head of the county.

''Blowing up the ice dam, of course!''

The Zhaicun villagers confirmed this as one.

''Then they'll have a monument too! We want to cherish their memories forever the same as Zhai Laosong!''

''Then apart from the relief fund,'' butted in Zhai Laogen, ''The county will have to give us enough cash for three monuments. Let's see ... brick tombs, granite steles, then the coffins will have to be made. Add labour costs.... If you want it all done nicely, there won't be much change out of three to four thousand yuan!''

''As much as that?'' The head of the county pondered it over a moment, then made up his mind: ''Okay! Now you'll be needing to choose another village leader!''

Having just heard Zhai Laogen in action and seen how he could get things done, the villagers were unanimous in their choice.

"Choose him! Zhai Laogen! He's a Party member...."

Twenty kilometres downstream, a resident of another village discovered Qianzi's rolled up cotton-padded jacket. Opening it up, his delight knew no bounds.

The three thousand yuan were soaked through. To dry them out, he spread them over two *kangs* in his home. His wife couldn't keep her mouth shut she was laughing so much.

He warned his two children: "You'd better not mention this to anyone!"

The children nodded their heads solemnly.

Two very grown-up children.

"Jinsuo, did you see Dad die?"

"Mmm."

"Tell me about it."

"There's nothing to tell."

"You're lying. You didn't see a thing!"

"Yes I did!" he yelled back obstinately at his elder sister.

"I saw everything."

"Tell me then! How did my husband die? Tell me ... how your Auntie Qianzi died...."

Jinsuo said nothing else, just turned and ran off towards the mountain pass. Facing the emptiness between the gorges he yelled: "Dad, they're going to build monuments for the three of you! Three beautiful monuments! Can you hear me, dad?"

Not long afterwards the relief funds from the county reached the Zhaicun villagers.

Zhai Laogen said to them, "This place is unlucky. Who knows, it might happen again, so it's best to split the funds and go off to find somewhere safer."

The villagers all agreed that what he said made a lot of sense, and so they split the funds there and then. Including the four thousand yuan monument money.

From then on, no one called Zhai lived in the area where there had once been a Zhaicun Village.

The Zhaicun villagers split up and departed to all points of the compass.

There was only one person that they bore any gratitude to. It wasn't Zhai Laosong, nor was it Maosheng or Qianzi.

It was Zhai Laogen.

If ever they bumped into each other they would ask: "Where's Laogen these days? He was a good bloke! You might not notice it normally, but when it came to the crunch he was all right! He didn't let the head of the county worry him!"

"Yes, yes…. If it hadn't been for him we would never have got that extra four thousand yuan to share out!"

No one knew where Zhai Laogen had gone, but he's doubtless still kicking about somewhere.

Xiumei had refused her share of the money.

Taking her younger brother with her, she left for distant parts.

Zhai Laogen never mentioned her refusing her share to anyone….

That winter, a bored crow pecked at a tiny little pointed and twisted shoe that was dangling from the branch of a tree.

The shoe belonged to Zhai Laogen's mother.

There was still something frozen stuck inside the shoe and it was this that had pricked the listless crow's interest. It was this that made him take the trouble to peck, peck, peck....

Suddenly something else caught his interest. Looking across he saw that someone had piled up three burial mounds and that a woman and a boy were offering sacrifice.

The two lines of footsteps came from very very far across the snow.

Translated by Christopher Smith

黑钮扣

梁晓声

熊猫丛书

*

中国文学出版社出版
(中国北京百万庄路 24 号)
中国国际图书贸易总公司发行
(中国北京车公庄西路 35 号)
北京邮政信箱第 399 号　　邮政编码 100044
1992 第 1 版　（英）
ISBN 7−5071−0116−9/1.108 (外)
00800
10−E−2789P